Issued under the authority of the Hor

Manual of
Firemansh

A survey of the science of fire-fighting

Book 9
Fire protection
of buildings

P.J. SALKILLD
JUNE 1984.

London
Her Majesty's Stationery Office

First published in 1977
Second impression 1978
Third impression 1979
Fourth impression 1984
The previous publishing history of
this volume is shown on pages 185/7

ISBN 0 11 340589 8

Preface

Information on the fire protection of buildings with regard to the detection, the giving of an alarm and the attack on a fire by fixed installations and equipment, previously contained in two separate volumes of the *Manual of Firemanship, Parts 4 and 5,* has been collated and extended in this 'Book'.

The advent of high-bay warehouses, the development of supersonic aircraft construction with their associated risks and the introduction of automatic ventilation and air pressurisation in buildings, have presented new problems in providing built-in protection. Reference is made to these.

Attention is drawn to the changes in terms previously known with regard to foam and reference to the 'Terminology' on Page 179 is necessary to acquaint students with the current British Standards Institute recommended terms; (reference is recommended to the Preface, *Manual of Firemanship, Book 3, 'Fire extinguishing equipment'*, in which these terms are explained).

It is to be noted that the orifice sizes for sprinkler heads (Table 7) are the metric sizes determined by the 'Rules of the Fire Offices' Committee for Automatic Sprinkler Installations, 29th Edition'.

It is to be appreciated that continuing development and design in the automatic fire detection field, which includes many and varied types, presents difficulties in fully describing each and every one separately. Therefore the alternative approach has been adopted whereby the various principles are explained and specific examples given. However it is important that fire service personnel involved in this particular type of work should be aware that many developments are taking place and constant reference to fire prevention and technical publications, manufacturers leaflets etc. is advised.

An additional feature of this 'Book' is the introduction on Page 181 of a list of technical publications related to certain material in the text. It is hoped that this will assist students who may wish to further their knowledge beyond the scope of this volume.

The Home Office wishes to record appreciation for the assistance given by other departments, manufacturers and organisations in compiling this 'Book'.

Home Office
December 1975

Metrication

List of SI units for use in the fire service.

Quantity and basic or derived SI unit and symbol	Approved unit of measurement	Conversion factor
Length metre (m)	kilometre (km) metre (m) millimetre (mm)	1 mile = 1.609 km 1 yard = 0.914 m 1 foot = 0.305 m 1 inch = 25.4 mm
Area square metre (m^2)	square kilometre (km^2) square metre (m^2) square millimetre (mm^2)	1 $mile^2$ = 2.590 km^2 1 $yard^2$ = 0.836 m^2 1 $foot^2$ = 0.093 m^2 1 $inch^2$ = 645.2 mm^2
Volume cubic metre (m^3)	cubic metre (m^3) litre (l) ($10^{-3}m^3$)	1 cubic foot = 0.028 m^3 1 gallon = 4.546 litres
Volume, flow cubic metre per second (m^3/s)	cubic metre per second (m^3/s) litres per minute ($l/min = 10^{-3}m^3/min$)	1 $foot^3/s$ = 0.028 m^3/s 1 gall/min = 4.546 l/min
Mass kilogram (kg)	kilogram (kg) tonne (t) = (10^3 kg)	1 lb. = 0.454 kg 1 ton = 1.016 t
Velocity metre per second (m/s)	metre/second (m/s) International knot (kn) kilometre/hour (km/h)	1 foot/second = 0.305 m/s 1 UK knot = 1.853 km/h 1 Int. knot = 1.852 km/h 1 mile/hour = 1.61 km/h
Acceleration metre per second^2 (m/s^2)	metre/second^2 (m/s^2)	1 foot/second^2 = 0.305 m/s^2 'g' = 9.81 m/s^2

Quantity and basic or derived SI unit and symbol	Approved unit of measurement	Conversion factor
Force newton (N)	kilonewton (kN) newton (N)	1 ton force = 9.964 kN 1 lb force = 4.448 N
Energy, work joule (J) (= 1 Nm)	joule (J) kilojoule (kJ) kilowatt-hour (kW h)	1 British thermal unit = 1.055 kJ 1 foot lb force = 1.356 J
Power watt (W) (= 1 J/s = 1 Nm/s)	kilowatt (kW) watt (W)	1 horsepower = 0.746 kW 1 foot lb force/second = 1.356 W
Pressure newton/metre² (N/m²) = 1 pascal (Pa)	bar = 10^5 N/m² millibar (mbar) (= 10^2 N/m²) metrehead	1 atmosphere = 101.325 kN/m² = 1.013 bar 1 lb force/in² = 6894.76 N/m² = 0.069 bar 1 inch Hg = 33.86 mbar 1 metrehead = 0.0981 bar 1 foot head = 0.305 metrehead
Heat, quantity of heat joule (J)	joule (J) kilojoule (kJ)	1 British thermal unit = 1.055 kJ
Heat flow rate watt (W)	watt (W) kilowatt (kW)	1 British thermal unit/ hour = 0.293 W 1 British thermal unit/ second = 1.055 kW
Specific energy, calorific value, specific latent heat joule/kilogram (J/kg) joule/m³ (J/m³)	kilojoule/kilogram (kJ/kg) kilojoule/m³ (kJ/m³) megajoule/m³ (MJ/m³)	1 British thermal unit/ lb = 2.326 kJ/kg 1 British thermal unit/ft³ = 37.26 kJ/m³
Temperature degree Celsius (°C)	degree Celsius (°C)	1 degree centigrade = 1 degree Celsius

Contents

Part 1
Fire extinguishing systems

Part 2
Fire alarm systems

Part 3
Fire venting systems

List of plates

15   An ultra-violet detector and amplifier—(detector 178 mm × 127 mm).
Photo: Honeywell Ltd

16   A 'Dimac' heat detector—(approximately 203 mm × 76 mm).

17   A break-link cable heat detector.
Photo: Sound Diffusion Ltd

18   A 'Pyrene 30D' heat detector—(63 mm × 57 mm).

19   A 'Fidela' heat detector—(197 mm × 57 mm).

20   A 'May-Oatway Mk 1' heat detector—(2.2 metres × 152 mm).
Photo: AFA-Minerva (EMI) Ltd

21   'Gents 1151' heat detector—(115 mm diameter × 38 mm).

22   A 'Pyrene' rate-of-rise detector—(61 mm × 57 mm).

23   A 'Fyrindex' automatic fire detector—(90 mm diameter × 51 mm).
Photo: Walter Kidde Co Ltd

24   A detector head used in the Kidde pneumatic system (approx. 115 mm × 76 mm).
Photo: Walter Kidde Co Ltd

25   An infra-red beam detector—the units—(250 mm × 150 mm).
Photo: Chubb Fire Security Ltd

26   An infra-red beam detector—emitter (interior).
Photo: Chubb Fire Security Ltd

27   An infra-red beam detector—receiver (interior).
Photo: Chubb Fire Security Ltd

28   A rotary gong.
Photo: AFA-Minerva (EMI) Ltd

29   A manual call point.
Photo: Chloride Gent Ltd

30   A manual call point—press button type.
Photo: Chloride Gent Ltd

31   A manual call point—with hammer.

32   A manual call point—key type.
Photo: Chloride Gent Ltd

33   A luminous indicator panel/control unit.
Photo: Chloride Gent Ltd

34   A more sophisticated type of luminous indicator panel/control unit.
Photo: AFA-Minerva (EMI) Ltd

35   A luminous indicator panel with building plan adjacent.
Photo: Honeywell Ltd

36   A signal selection unit.

37 Close up of one type of automatic fire ventilator showing pneumatic ram and stainless steel opening spring (captive until freed by fusible link). Link is hidden by conical shield which prevents sprinkler water cooling the link.
Photo: Colt International Ltd

38 A twin-door roof vent operated by a fusible link.
Photo: Argosy Engineering Ltd

39 A further example of a twin-door roof vent operated by a fusible link.
Photo: Powrmatic Ltd

40 Fireman's over-ride control for testing operation of fire vent installation or to open vent in advance of fusing temperature being reached.
Photo: Colt International Ltd

41 Automatic fire ventilators on the roof of an automated high-bay warehouse. (Note—Small inclined rain-sensing panel on vent in left foreground.)
Photo: Colt International Ltd

42 The 'Type A' vertical fire/seal steel curtain fire damper shown open.
Photo: Ozonair Engineering Co Ltd

43 The 'Type A' vertical fire/seal steel curtain fire damper shown closed.
Photo: Ozonair Engineering Co Ltd

44 An intumescent damper as seen before a fire.
Photo: Fire Research Station

45 An intumescent damper (same face as in Plate 44) after fire.
Photo: Fire Research Station

46 The same intumescent damper (as in Plates 44 and 45) showing the effect when fire approaches from the reverse side.
Photo: Fire Research Station

Note—The measurements given in brackets in the captions are to assist in relating the photograph to actual size.

Part 1
Fire extinguishing systems

The provision of fixed pipework systems using water as the extinguishing medium is acknowledged to be an efficient means of protecting buildings and many other classes of risk against extensive damage resulting from an outbreak of fire. Such systems can be divided into three main classes—automatic sprinklers, drenchers (external sprinklers) and water spray projector systems.

Automatic sprinklers are installed inside a building and operate when a fire occurs. Drenchers, which may be automatically or manually operated, are fitted outside a building in order to protect it from fire in a nearby property. Water spray projector systems are a specialised development of automatic fire protection. These are designed for extinguishing fires involving oils or similar flammable liquids. Automatic sprinklers, drenchers and other installations using water are dealt with in Chapters 1 to 7.

There are, however, other fixed installation extinguishing systems not using water, such as foam, carbon dioxide, vaporising liquids, dry powders and inert gases, which are designed specifically for the protection of special risks. These are detailed in Chapter 8.

Finally some extinguishing systems have been specially adapted to deal with unusual risks, such as high-bay warehouses, and these developments are detailed in Chapter 9.

Chapter 1
Automatic sprinklers: principles of design

Since a most important principle of successful fire extinction is to attack an outbreak immediately, it follows that any device which can detect a fire automatically and then help to extinguish it with a minimum of fire loss will prove of great value. Automatic sprinkler systems using water as the extinguishing medium have been universally adopted for this purpose. This type of apparatus has been in use for over one hundred years and has been installed in thousands of buildings throughout the world.

Basically an automatic sprinkler installation comprises a system of pipes erected at or near the ceiling of each floor of a building and connected through controlling valves to one or more water supplies. At intervals in the pipework, at varying distances according to the classification of the premises, are sealed outlets called sprinklers or sprinkler heads. These contain a device whereby a rise in temperature to a predetermined limit causes the sprinkler to open and water to be discharged in the form of a spray over an area of the floor below the sprinkler. The sprinklers are so spaced that, in the event of two or more heads operating simultaneously, the area sprayed by each sprinkler overlaps that sprayed by its neighbour, thus leaving no part of the floor unprotected.

The operation of the head leads to the opening of a valve and causes an alarm bell to ring (and in some installations a direct call to the fire brigade), so drawing attention to the outbreak. The layout of a typical sprinkler system is shown in Fig. 1.1.

1 Historical

A system of roses or perforated shallow pans connected to pipes controlled by valves already closed by string was invented in England in 1806 by John Carey, but does not seem to have been used. The system operated when these valves opened as a result of the burning of the string. Later, manually-operated systems using perforated pipes and roses were constructed and around the mid-century, perforated pipe systems were extensively employed in New England cotton mills. Patents were taken out in many countries for systems of automatic extinction. The first automatic sprinkler appears to have been invented by William Macbay in 1852; this was followed by a much more practical device invented by Lewis Roughton in 1861.

There is no evidence of use of either of these devices. Major A. Stuart Harrison of the First Engineers London Volunteers, invented the first sensitive automatic sprinkler in 1864 (i.e. a sprinkler in which the fusible element was not in contact with the water) but this head, although demonstrated from time to time, was never exploited. The type first to be commercially exploited was that invented by an American, Henry Parmelee, in 1874. Numerous and varied types followed, including that introduced in the United States of America by Frederick Grinnell in 1882. Both types incorporated a fusible soldered link which melted under the influence of heat and released water from the system through the head. From this early design many modern solder-type heads have been developed.

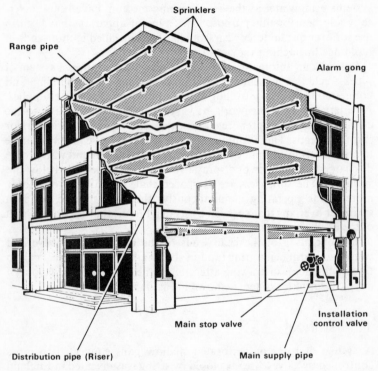

Fig. 1.1 Layout of a typical sprinkler installation.

Shortly after the First World War, two major developments took place: the introduction of the multiple control system and of the glass bulb sprinkler head. The multiple control system comprises open distributors evenly spaced at the ceilings and connected together on uncharged pipes in groups of not more than eight. The pipes feeding the controls are charged with water under pressure and the operation of a control releases water to the distributors which discharge it uniformly over the area covered by the group. The system will be found in risks such as paint works where the possibility of liquid fuel fires on the floor demands an immediate even water spray distribution over an area greater than that covered by a single sprinkler.

The glass bulb sprinkler embodies a cylindrical or barrel-shaped bulb made of a strong glass and containing a liquid which expands when heated until, at a pre-determined temperature, it shatters the bulb into small fragments and allows the immediate and free opening of the head. The contents of the bulb are not liable to freeze and the head can be installed in any situation. The advantage of this type of sprinkler is that the bulb is not liable to corrosion. A further innovation is a head developed in the United States of America in which the solder takes the form of a pellet under compression, the melting of which permits the head to open.

Efforts have been made to perfect a system by which the water would automatically be turned off when the fire has been extinguished. One such system has been developed: the 're-cycling pre-action system' (see page 28), but it is essential that the work of the fire service should supplement the automatic action of a sprinkler system, to ensure that all pockets of fire are dealt with and that the water is not turned off until the fire service officer in charge gives instructions to that effect.

At the time of publication of this volume of the *Manual*, there is no national legislation compelling owners of property to install sprinkler systems in buildings, although under local legislation in force in some areas, plans of certain types of building, such as theatres, cinemas, large department stores and factories, will only receive approval if adequate provision for sprinklers is made. Certain requirements under the Building Regulations can be waived where sprinkler systems are fitted in accordance with the appropriate standard.

The insurance companies encourage the installation of sprinkler systems by giving substantial reductions in premiums for buildings so equipped. The insurance companies, through the Fire Offices' Committee, lay down minimum standards necessary to secure premium rebates.

2   Principles of design

Sprinkler systems are invariably designed in accordance with:

(i)   British Standard 5306 Pt. 2,

(ii) The Rules of the Fire Offices' Committee for Automatic Sprinkler Installations.

The Code of Practice makes general recommendations on design of component parts, materials used, inspection and maintenance. In all cases where insurance is involved, the systems must be installed and maintained according to the Fire Offices' Committee Rules. These rules were revised in 1973 following some years of research which was carried out in several different countries involving extensive tests at Fire Research Stations and practical tests in buildings. A study was also made of insurance statistics and the history of sprinkler systems. Based on this research, systems are now 'tailor made' to suit a particular occupancy and the system is designed to produce a certain density of water spray over a pre-determined area for a given period of time depending on the expected area of fire development in that particular occupancy.

The Code of Practice and the Fire Offices' Committee Rules ensure that a sprinkler system is installed to a high standard and failures seldom occur. Failures which do occur are largely due to faults brought about by the use of the building, such as structural alterations, installation of new plant, redecoration and change of occupancy, mechanical damage to the system or lack of maintenance.

Sprinkler installations are used to protect a wide range of premises. There are very few buildings which are totally unsuitable for sprinklers. Where parts of premises contain materials and processes for which water would be unsuitable as an extinguishing medium, these parts can be isolated from the rest of the building by fire-resisting construction. The remainder of the premises is then fitted with sprinklers.

3 Risk categories

The Fire Offices' Committee arranges occupancies into risk categories, each having an accepted abbreviation. These are shown in Table 1.

Table 1
Fire Offices' Committee risk categories

Category	Abbreviation
Extra light hazard	XLH
Ordinary hazard: Group 1	OH1
Ordinary hazard: Group 2	OH2
Ordinary hazard: Group 3	OH3
Ordinary hazard: Group 3 Special	OH3(S)
Extra high hazard	XHH

a. Extra light hazard (XLH)
These are premises containing hazards of the non-industrial type, i.e. offices, libraries, etc. where the amount and combustibility of the contents is low.

b. Ordinary hazards: OH1, OH2, OH3, OH3(S)

Ordinary hazards are commercial and industrial premises involving the handling, processing and storage of a wide range of mainly combustible materials which are unlikely to burn intensely in the early stages of a fire. A very wide range of fire risks fall into this category and it has been necessary to sub-divide them into four groups, as indicated above.

c. Extra high hazard (XHH)

This category covers commercial and industrial occupancies having abnormal fire loads:

(i)   where the materials handled or processed are mainly of an extra hazardous nature likely to develop rapid and intensely-burning fires (*process risks*);

(ii) involving the high piling of goods (*high-piled storage risks*).

According to the hazardous nature of the stock and the height of the storage, 'high-piled storage risks' are sub-divided into four categories:

Category I

Category II   (For specific detailed lists in each category, see
Rules of the Fire Offices' Committee for Auto-
Category III   matic Sprinkler Installations, 29th Edition).

Category IV

The term 'storage' includes the warehousing or the temporary depositing of goods or materials whilst undergoing processing.

4 Classes of system

Three classes of sprinkler system have been developed to suit the above risk categories and are called:

(a)   extra light hazard system;

(b)   ordinary hazard system, and

(c)   extra high hazard system.

Pipework for two or more different types of 'hazard system' may be connected to a common set of control valves provided the total number of sprinklers does not exceed the permitted maximum. Each of these systems has been designed to give an appropriate density of discharge over an assumed maximum area of operation in the highest and most hydraulically-remote parts of a protected building.

The density of discharge and the assumed maximum area of operation for the three classes are as follows:

a. Extra light hazard system

Density of discharge: 2.25 mm/min.
Assumed maximum area of operation: 84 m².
For certain areas of 'extra light hazard' occupancies, such as attics, basements, boiler rooms, kitchens, laundries, storage areas and workrooms, the density of discharge may be increased to 5 mm/min.

b. Ordinary hazard system

Density of discharge: 5 mm/min.
Ordinary hazard systems have been graded into four groups on the basis of the assumed maximum area of operation:

Group 1 (light ordinary hazard OH1):   72 m²

Group 2 (medium ordinary hazard OH2): 144 m²

Group 3 (high ordinary hazard OH3): 216 m²

Group 3 Special (OH3(S)): 360 m²

c. Extra high hazard system

(1) Process risks
Density of discharge: 7.5 to 12.5 mm/min.
Assumed maximum area of operation: 260 m².

(2) High piled storage risks
Density of discharge: 7.5 to 30 mm/min.
Assumed maximum area of operation: 260 to 300 m².

Chapter 2
Automatic sprinklers: water supplies

Automatic sprinkler systems must be provided with a suitable and acceptable water supply. The Fire Offices' Committee Rules lay down the following as being accepted sources of water supply:

(i)   town mains;

(ii) elevated private reservoirs;

(iii) gravity tanks;

(iv) automatic pump supply;

(v)   pressure tanks.

Compliance with certain requirements is necessary in respect of each of these sources of supply. The town main is the most common and, when forming one of two or more supplies to a sprinkler system, is usually the primary or principal one.

1 General requirements

The water supply must have a pressure and flow characteristic not less than that specified in the Fire Offices' Committee Rules. It must be automatic, thoroughly reliable and not subject to either frost or drought conditions that could seriously affect the supply. The supply should be under the control of the occupier of the building containing the installation or, where this is not practicable, the right of use of the supply must be suitably guaranteed.

The water must be free from any matter in suspension which would be liable to cause accumulations in the system pipework. The use of salt or brackish water is not normally allowed. In special circumstances where there is no suitable fresh water source available, consideration may be given to the use of salt or brackish water provided that the installation is normally charged with fresh water.

2 Grading of systems according to water supplies available

Sprinkler systems are divided into three grades according to the number and type of water supplies available.

a. Grade I

Grade I systems have duplicate water supplies, or one 'superior'* water supply provided the total number of sprinklers (excluding those in concealed spaces) in the protected building or range of buildings does not exceed 2000 with not more than 200 sprinklers (excluding those in concealed spaces) in each separate risk†.

b. Grade II

Grade II systems have one 'superior' water supply without the limitations on the number of sprinklers mentioned in (a) above.

c. Grade III

These have a single water supply from a town main or automatic pump. Grade III water supplies are not normally accepted for extra high hazard systems.

3 Superior water supplies

a. Town mains

The mains water supply must be fed from both ends by mains, each of which must be capable of sustaining the required pressure and flow. Duplicated connections from the main must be carried separately to the premises which contain the sprinkler installation, and there should be a stop valve on the main between the two branches.

In the event of fracture or partial breakdown of the main, operation of the stop valves ensures that the supply is maintained by that part of the main which is still functioning. The mains at each end must not be directly dependent on a common trunk main in the town main system, and this must be fed from more than one source. The main must be capable of furnishing at all times of the day and night the minimum pressure and flow requirements for the appropriate category of risk. If it is not possible to provide duplicate connections, special consideration may be given to the waiving of the requirement if there is a stop valve (secured open) on the town main immediately on each side of a single branch connection.

b. Elevated private reservoir

This is simply defined as similar to a ground reservoir but situated at a higher level than the premises to be protected. Certain conditions regarding capacity must be complied with before this type of reservoir can be used as a source of supply to a sprinkler installation. The minimum capacity ranges from 9 m^3 to 875 m^3 depending on the

---

* 'Superior' water supplies are those listed under Section 3.
† A separate risk is defined as a risk separated from the rest of the building by a fire-resisting structure.

class of system installed; this is on the understanding that the stored water is used entirely for the sprinkler system.

Where such reservoirs serve other than sprinkler installations, e.g. water for trade and domestic purposes, there must be a constant capacity of at least:

500 m^3 in XLH categories;
1000 m^3 in OH categories;
1000 m^3 plus the stored capacity 225 to 875 m^3 in XHH categories (according to design density).

In certain cases smaller capacities may be accepted. The Fire Offices' Committee must approve all relevant details.

c. Gravity tank

A gravity tank (Plate 1) is defined as a purpose-built container. It is erected on the site of the protected premises at such a height as to provide the requisite pressure and flow condition at the installation valves and needs to be adequately protected against freezing. Where the tank is not enclosed within a tower, the top must be covered in such a manner so as to exclude daylight and solid matter.

The main provisions are: ·

(i) The tank must have a minimum capacity of 9 m^3 for the extra light hazard class rising to 875 m^3 for the extra high hazard class where the design density of discharge is 30 mm/min. Should the capacity of the tank exceed these requirements, it is permissible to draw upon the surplus for other purposes by means of an outlet pipe which must be taken out of the side of the tank above the level of the quantity to be reserved for the sprinkler installation.

(ii) The quantity of water· required for the sprinkler installation must be automatically maintained. If the tank forms the sole supply to the system, the supply to the tank must be capable of refilling to the required capacity within six hours.

(iii) The tank must be fitted with an indicator showing the depth of water; the water must be kept clean and free from sediment.

(iv) The use of one tank to supply installations in two or more buildings under separate ownership is not allowed.

d. Automatic pump supply

If a water supply is available with no head or only under limited pressure, a pump may be used to feed water into the installation at the required pressure. In such cases, it is stipulated that the supply shall be from a virtually inexhaustible source, such as a river, canal, lake, or it may be from two limited capacity suction tanks. The primary suction tank must have a holding capacity equal to that required for the particular hazard class. The secondary suction tank may be of smaller capacity with automatic inflow provided it meets Fire Offices' Committee requirements, or the supply can be from a single limited capacity suction tank where the circumstances are considered favourable.

The most important provisions relating to pumps are as follows:

(i)   With an automatic pump supply consisting of two automatic pumps, at least one must be driven by a compression ignition (diesel) engine with each pump capable of providing the required pressure and flow independently. With three automatic pumps, at least two must have a compression ignition drive. Any two pumps together must be capable of providing the necessary pressures and flows. In both arrangements they must be capable of operating in parallel, i.e. with similar pressure and flow characteristics.

(ii) The pump must be housed in a readily accessible position in a sprinkler-protected building, or in the case of an electric motor-driven pump, it must be housed in a separate building of non-combustible construction used for no purpose other than for the housing of fire protection water supplies. It must be adequately protected against mechanical damage. The temperature of the room should be maintained above 4°C (10°C where compression ignition engines are used).

(iii) Automatic priming equipment must be provided where necessary to ensure that the pump will be fully primed with water at all times.

(iv) The performance characteristics of the pumps should be such that the pressure falls progressively with the rate of demand. They must be capable of providing the rate of flow and pressure required at the highest and most remote parts of the protected premises. The output must be so controlled that there is not an excessive rate of discharge at the lowest level in areas close to the installation valves. To meet these conditions pumps must have performance characteristics complying with the requirements laid down.

(v)   Where permitted by the water authority, a pump may draw directly from a town main, provided the latter is capable of supplying water at all times at the maximum rated output of the pump.

(vi) The pump should be fully operational within 30 seconds after starting.

12

(vii) The pump should have a direct drive and must start automatically. Means should be provided for manual starting and once started the pump must run continuously until stopped manually.

(viii) Where an automatic pump forms the sole supply, a fall in water pressure in the sprinkler system, which is intended to initiate the automatic starting of the pump, shall at the same time provide a visual and audible alarm at some suitable location, e.g. in the gatehouse or by the installation control valves.

(ix) A test for the automatic starting of the pump must be carried out weekly.

(x) Pumps must be driven either by an electric motor or an approved compression ignition type engine. The electric supply must be obtained from a reliable source, preferably from a public supply. Where a compression ignition engine is used, provision must be made for two separate methods of engine starting. It is preferable that centrifugal pumps should be fixed at least 600 mm below the minimum storage level of the water supply.

(xi) Any switches to the electric power feed to motors must be clearly labelled: 'Sprinkler pump motor supply—not to be switched off in the event of fire.'

e. Pressure tank

A pressure tank is an acceptable superior water supply for XLH and OH1 categories only, *provided*:

(i) The water capacity is not less than:

Sole supply: 7 m^3 for XLH; 23 m^3 for OH1.

Duplicate supply: 7 m^3 for XLH; 15 m^3 for OH—all groups.

(ii) There is an approved arrangement for maintaining automatically the required air pressure and water level into the tank under non-fire conditions.

4 Duplicate water supplies

A duplicate water supply, where required, must be capable of providing the same pressure, rate of flow and have the same capacity as that required for the primary supply. In the case of extra light and ordinary hazard classes only, a pressure tank will be accepted as one source of a duplicate water supply.

The following combinations of water supplies are approved duplicate water supplies:

(i) Two town mains.

(ii) Town main and pressure tank (extra light and ordinary hazard classes only).

(iii) Town main and elevated private reservoir or gravity tank.

(iv) Town main and automatic pump.

(v) Automatic pump and pressure tank (extra light and ordinary hazard classes only).

(vi) Automatic pump and elevated private reservoir or gravity tank—provided the latter does not form the source of supply to the automatic pump.

(vii) Two elevated private reservoirs or gravity tanks.

(viii) Automatic pump supply drawing from:

    (a) A virtually inexhaustible source, such as a river, canal, lake, etc.

    (b) Two limited capacity suction tanks; the primary suction tank must have a holding capacity at least equal to that required for the relevant hazard class; the secondary suction tank may be of smaller capacity with automatic inflow provided it satisfies certain requirements. (Where limited capacity suction tanks are used the FOC rules state specific requirements as to the number, and certain requirements as to the type, of pump to be used).

    (c) A single suction tank, but consideration will only be given to this if the circumstances are thought to be favourable.

(ix) Elevated private reservoir and pressure tank (extra light and ordinary hazard classes only).

5 Pressure tanks

A pressure tank (Plate 2) is a cylindrical steel vessel with convex ends filled with air under pressure and water. It is acceptable as a sole water supply in the case of extra light hazard class and ordinary hazard class—Group 1, but only as one source of a duplicate water supply in the case of ordinary hazard class—Groups 2, 3 and 3(S).

a. General

The general requirements for a pressure tank are:

(i) It must be housed in a readily accessible position in a sprinkler protected building or in a separate building of incombustible construction used for no purpose other than for the housing of fire protection water supplies. The tank must be adequately protected against mechanical damage. The temperature of the room should be maintained above 4°C.

(ii)   When used as a single water supply, the tank must be provided with an approved arrangement for maintaining automatically the required air pressure and water level in the tank under non-fire conditions. The arrangement should include an approved warning system to indicate failure of the devices to restore the correct pressure and water level. This arrangement is also advocated in cases where the tank provides the duplicate supply.

(iii) The tank must be fitted with air pressure gauges and a gauge glass to show the level of the water. Stop valves and back pressure valves must be provided on both the water and air supply connections to the tank and they must be fixed as close to the tank as possible (Fig. 2.1).

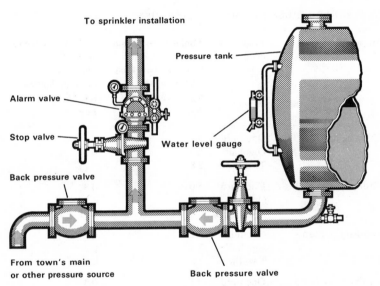

Fig. 2.1 Pressure tank and town main with back pressure valves.

(iv)   The minimum quantity of water to be maintained in the tank is:

When sole supply: extra light hazard class: 7 m^3
                         ordinary hazard class—Group 1: 23 m^3

When duplicate supply:
                         extra light hazard class: 7 m^3
                         ordinary hazard class—all groups: 15 m^3

In addition to these requirements, where a pressure tank forms the sole supply to an installation, connections are not allowed to be taken from the supply for any purpose other than sprinklers. If it forms the secondary supply, a pipe not exceeding 50 mm may be taken from the combined water supply main to supply hydraulic hose reels for fire-fighting purposes only, subject to the pressure being replenished automatically as in (ii) above.

b. Air pressure

The working air pressure for pressure tanks is shown in Table 2, and it will be seen from the table that the pressure in the tank stands at a comparatively high figure. Due to this high pressure, where it forms part of a duplicate water supply, it is often the first supply to be drawn upon and gives a strong initial discharge.

Table 2

Working air pressure for pressure tanks

Hazard class	Proportion of air in tank	Minimum air pressure to be maintained in tank when base is on a level with the highest sprinkler *bar*	Add for each metre or part thereof where the tank is below the highest sprinkler *bar*
Extra light	One-third	8.6	0.3
	One-half	5.4	0.2
	Two-thirds	3.8	0.15
Ordinary: Group 1	One-third	5.0	0.3
	One-half	3.0	0.2
	Two-thirds	2.0	0.15
Ordinary: Group 2	One-third	6.2	0.3
	One-half	3.8	0.2
	Two-thirds	2.6	0.15
Ordinary: Group 3	One-third	7.1	0.3
	One-half	4.4	0.2
	Two-thirds	3.0	0.15
Ordinary: Group 3(S)	One-third	8.0	0.3
	One-half	5.0	0.2
	Two-thirds	3.5	0.15

6   Pressure and flow requirements

The Fire Offices' Committee Rules lay down the minimum requirements for pressure and flow in a sprinkler system. These vary for each risk category.

a. Extra light and ordinary hazard classes

For extra light and ordinary hazard classes, the figure is made up of:

(i) an *actual* pressure figure (at the installation control valve),

PLUS

(ii) a *calculated* pressure figure (based on the difference in height between the highest sprinklers and the valves at specified rates of water discharge).

Table 3 lists the relevant figures.

Table 3

Pressure and flow requirements

Risk category	(i) Actual pressure Minimum required running pressure*	(ii) Plus calculated pressure Based on height between highest sprinkler and valves when rate of flow is:
	bar	*dm³/min†*
Extra light hazard	2.2	225
Ordinary: Group 1	1.0	375
	0.7	540
Ordinary: Group 2	1.4	725
	1.0	1000
Ordinary: Group 3	1.7	1100
	1.4	1350
Ordinary: Group 3(S)	2.0	1800
	1.5	2100

* Measured on installation pressure gauge.

† 1 dm³/min = 1 litre/min.

b. Extra high hazard class

In the case of extra high hazard class (XHH) very full and specific figures are laid down in the Fire Offices' Committee Rules. The import of these figures is that the water supply must be capable of providing the required flow and corresponding running pressure, at the level of the highest sprinklers in the extra high hazard portion of the premises. The supply must also meet with the requisite density of discharge and area of operation specified for the particular class of occupancy.

B

7 Proving of water supplies

In the case of town mains, elevated private reservoirs and gravity tanks, facilities must be provided to enable proving tests to be carried out at the valves on each installation to verify that the water supply satisfies the requirements of pressure and flow specified for each hazard class. Water supplies from automatic pumps and pressure tanks are designed to meet the pressure and flow conditions appropriate to the hazard class and accordingly it is not necessary to require practical flow tests in these instances.

8 Fire brigade inlets

Sprinkler installations fed solely from water supplies of limited capacity, such as pressure tank or gravity tank supplies, must be fitted with a fire brigade inlet connection. This is to enable the fire brigade to pump water into the installation by the use of their own equipment. The fitting of fire brigade inlets to all other installations is also strongly recommended.

Chapter 3
Automatic sprinklers: protection systems

There are six types of standard sprinkler system. They are:

(1) Wet pipe.

(2) Dry pipe.

(3) Alternate wet and dry pipe.

(4) Tail-end dry pipe (used in conjunction with (1) or (2)).

(5) Tail-end alternate (used in conjunction with (1)).

(6) Pre-action.

In addition to these there is also what is known as the 'deluge system'.

1 Wet pipe system

In this system, the commonest and simplest in general use, all the pipes that lead from the water supplies through the various controlling valves to the sprinkler heads throughout the building are kept permanently filled with water. Wet pipe systems are installed in premises where there is no danger at any time of the water in the pipes freezing. The principal controls of such a system are:

(i) a stop valve on each separate source of supply;

(ii) a non-return valve on each source of supply;

(iii) an installation main stop valve to cut off the flow of water to the system after a head has opened and the fire has been extinguished;

(iv) an alarm valve, which lifts when water enters the sprinkler feed pipes and permits the passage of water to the alarm gong; this valve also acts as a non-return valve to prevent the return flow of water from the sprinkler pipes to the supply connections;

(v) a test and drain valve, used for inducing the water flow to the installation and to empty the system when necessary. The size of this valve is 40 mm in extra light hazard installations and 50 mm in extra high hazard installations.

a. Types of wet pipe installation

In Fig. 3.1 is shown a typical wet pipe installation in which it will be seen that there are two sources of supply, one from the towns main (1) and the other from a secondary source supply (2). Both are fitted with stop valves and with non-return valves to ensure that water from either supply will not flow into the other. These supplies unite in the main supply pipe (3) which is fitted with a main stop valve (4). Above the main stop valve is an alarm valve (5) from which a pipe is led off to the alarm motor and gong (6). When the alarm valve functions, some water passes through an annular groove in the alarm valve seating into the pipe to the water turbine, operating the latter and causing a clapper to strike the gong.

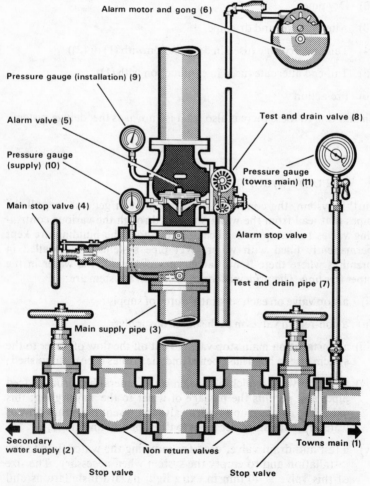

Fig. 3.1 A wet pipe system showing the main valves and gauges.

Adjacent to the alarm valve there is a test and drain pipe (7) leading off, and the discharge from this pipe is controlled by a test and drain valve (8). This valve fulfils the dual purpose of draining the installation and facilitating the testing of water supplies for running pressure.

There are three gauges, namely:

(i)   gauge (9) which shows the pressure in the installation itself above the main stop and alarm valves;

(ii)   gauge (10) which shows the pressure of the supply below the main stop valve;

(iii) gauge (11) which shows the pressure in the towns main.

A gauge indicating the pressure of the secondary supply is not considered necessary, except when the secondary supply is a towns main. Secondary supplies in the form of pumps require pressure gauges to be fitted.

Different types of wet pipe installation will be found installed in premises, but the general layout and principle of operation will be very similar to that described above.

Wet pipe systems are so designed that the number of sprinklers controlled by one set of valves (including tail end extensions) does not exceed 500 in extra light hazard systems, or 1000 in ordinary and extra high hazard systems; this latter figure is inclusive of any sprinklers on any extra light hazard system. In calculating the total number of sprinklers on wet pipe systems, the number of sprinklers in concealed spaces or in machines may be ignored. Where more heads than this are installed, two or more sets of installation valves should be employed. Each set of valves must have a number painted thereon, and the appropriate alarm gong must bear the same number in bold figures. In wet installations the sprinkler heads may be installed in either the upright (above the range pipes) or pendent position (fitted to the underside of the range pipes).

2   Dry pipe system

This type of system is only allowed in buildings where the temperature conditions are artificially maintained close to, or below, freezing point, such as in cold or cool stores and fur vaults, or where the temperature is maintained above 70°C, as in drying ovens. The pipes are at all times kept charged with air under sufficient pressure to hold back the water. The controlling valves of a dry pipe installation comprise a main stop valve, as in the wet pipe system, and a differential air valve, which is a substitute for the alarm valve in a wet system.

Also fitted are a hydraulic alarm motor and gong, test and drain valves, an alarm cock and pressure gauges.

a. Operation of the differential air valve

A differential air valve (Fig. 3.2) consists of two valves, one large and one small. The upper valve is eight times as large as the lower valve and is held in position by air pressure and a water seal. In theory the air pressure acting on the upper valve is capable of holding back a water pressure eight times as great, but in practice it is a little less than this. The area between the two sections of the valve is subject to atmospheric pressure.

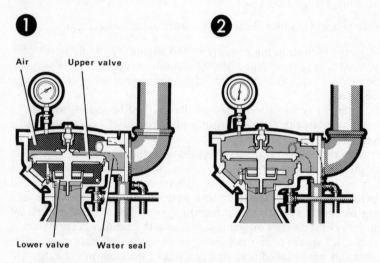

Fig. 3.2 The differential air valve of a dry pipe system. (1) In the closed position. (2) In the open position.

When a sprinkler head opens, the compressed air escapes thus reducing the pressure on the upper valve, eventually allowing the lower valve to open, so that water enters the system and emerges at the open sprinkler head. It will be appreciated, however, that there is some delay before the water reaches the sprinkler head on account of the time required to release sufficient air from the system to allow the valve to open and then the water to enter and travel up the pipe to the open sprinkler head. A device known as an accelerator is therefore normally fitted, or a special type of valve is incorporated, the function of which is to speed up the entry of water into the system. It is undesirable to maintain a greater air pressure in the system than is necessary, and approximately one-third to one-half of the maximum water pressure is the normal figure. Provision is made for replacing any slight leakage that takes place.

b. Action of the accelerator

The action of an accelerator varies with each make of differential valve. The type fitted to the Mather and Platt alternate system is taken as representative.

The accelerator consists of two vessels normally filled with air at the same pressure as that of the installation. The lower vessel (Fig. 3.3(1)) is connected directly to the installation through the pipe (2), but the upper vessel (3) has no direct communication with the installation except through the pinhole (4). When a sprinkler head operates, pressure in the upper vessel and the inter-connecting air chamber (5) falls less rapidly than in the lower vessel. Soon, therefore, the pressure exerted on each side of the diaphragm (6) becomes unequal and the diaphragm moves away from the air chamber. In doing so, it pushes the plunger (7) which in turn knocks over the bobweight (8) that opens the valve (9), thus allowing air to pass through the lower vessel, through the pipe (2) to the pipe (10), as shown by the arrows in Fig. 3.3 (right).

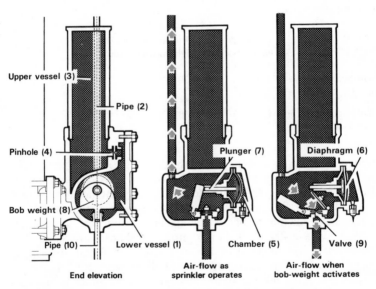

Fig. 3.3 Diagram showing the principles underlying the operation of an accelerator.

The pipe (10) leads into the atmospheric chamber between the upper and lower valves in the differential air valve and the pressure of air entering this chamber quickly neutralises the pressure holding the upper valve down, thus speeding up the opening process.

When an accelerator is fitted the time taken for the water to reach the fire is shorter as the time for the double clack valve to lift is reduced from about 2.5 minutes to about 20 seconds. Attempts to cut down this time still further may result in the valve lifting accidentally. It should be remembered that a further short time will elapse after the valve has opened, before the water reaches the sprinkler head that has actuated.

c. Maximum number of sprinklers

Dry pipe systems are so designed that the number of sprinklers controlled by one set of valves does not exceed the limits laid down for this type of system (Table 4). The sprinklers must be installed in the upright position above the range pipes, although an exception to this may be allowed if approved dry pendent pattern sprinklers (see page 44) are installed.

Table 4

Number of sprinklers permitted on alternate wet and dry pipe systems and dry pipe systems controlled by one set of valves

	Extra light hazard systems	Ordinary and/or extra high hazard systems
With accelerator or exhauster	250	500
Without accelerator or exhauster	125	250

Where a sprinkler system covers both categories, the maximum number of sprinklers is taken as that shown in the second column in Table 4, but in this event each head in the extra light hazard section is counted as two. So a combined system with an accelerator would be permitted a maximum of 500 on paper; in practice, however, it could only have 400 heads. For example, if 300 heads are required in the ordinary hazard (OH) section, this leaves 200 for the extra light hazard (ELH) section, but as each of these will count double, a further 100 heads only can be installed, giving a maximum of 500.

3 Alternate wet and dry system

This system is usually installed in premises without adequate artificial heating where the water in the pipes of a wet system would be liable to freeze during cold weather. It usually operates on the wet principle in the summer and the dry principle in the winter. When functioning on the wet system, the dry valve is either changed over or placed out of commission and the system functions as a wet system. Changing the system from one method of operation to the other can be effected quickly. A wet system is to be preferred since statistics show that when fires occur, a greater number of heads open when the system is on air, due to the delay in water reaching the first sprinkler head affected.

a. Sprinkler heads

In dry pipe and alternate systems the sprinkler heads are always placed above the distributing pipes, which are themselves given a slight slope so that water will not be trapped in pockets when the system is drained. The only exception to this rule which is allowed is if approved dry pendent pattern sprinklers are installed or where standard sprinkler erected pendents have an approved anti-freeze device incorporated in them.

b. Valve assembly

A typical alternate system valve assembly with the valve clacks lifting vertically on a central spindle is shown in Fig. 3.4. This pattern has the accelerator (1) separate from the main part of the assembly.

When set up as in Fig. 3.4, the pipes of the installation are filled with air. The water pressure is shown on the supply pressure gauge (2) and the air pressure on the installation pressure gauge (3). The main stop valve (4) is open and the water is held back by the differential air valve (5 and 6), as described on page 22.

c. Three-way cock

It should be noted that the three-way cock (Fig. 3.4(7)) is adjusted differently when the installation is on the wet pipe system than when it is on the dry pipe system. When on the dry system, as shown in the illustration, the three-way cock must be set to allow water from the atmospheric chamber (8) to flow through pipe (9) and then into the alarm pipe. On the wet system, however, the pipe (9) is disconnected and, as soon as the alarm valve (11) is actuated, water flows through the pipe (12) past the cock and into the alarm pipe (10). The correct setting can be obtained by making the grooves on the face of the cock correspond with the water passages it is desired to open.

The double clack of the air valve can only be reset by hand. For this purpose the hand hole cover (13) is provided. This cover must not be removed to reset the valve until the main stop valve (4) has been shut and the installation drained; otherwise the room where the valves are located will immediately be flooded.

d. Changing the installation from the wet to the dry system

The steps to be followed to change each system vary in detail, and an instruction card is usually provided by the installing engineers; this should be found hanging near the main stop valve. Changing an installation will invariably be the responsibility of the occupiers of the premises or perhaps the installing engineers; members of the fire service will not normally be involved.

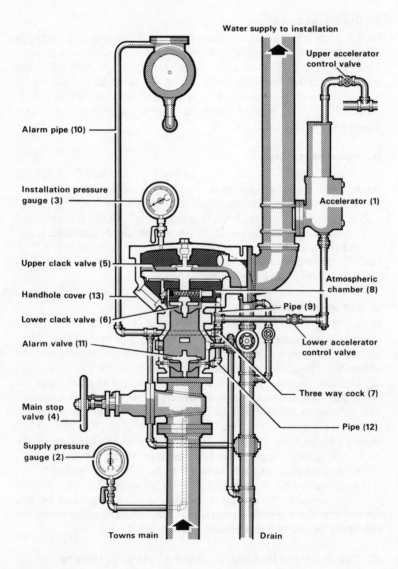

Fig. 3.4 Cross-section through the air valve and alarm valve of an alternate sprinkler system.

4 Tail-end systems (dry pipe or alternate)

These systems are essentially similar to those previously described, except that they are of comparatively small extent and form extensions to standard sprinkler installations. They are permitted:

(a) As extensions to a wet pipe system in comparatively small areas (i) where there is possible frost danger in an otherwise adequately heated building, and (ii) in high temperature areas or stoves. The tail-end would be on the alternate wet and dry pipe principle in the case of (i) and on the dry pipe principle for (ii).

(b) As extensions to an alternate wet and dry pipe system in high temperature areas or stoves, when the tail-end systems would be on the dry pipe principle.

Sprinklers in tail-end systems must be installed in the upright position above the lines of pipes, an exception being if approved dry pendent pattern sprinklers are installed.

The number of sprinklers in a group of tail-end systems controlled by one set of wet pipe system or alternate wet and dry pipe system valves, must not exceed 250 in the aggregate, with not more than 100 sprinklers on any one tail-end system. Each tail-end system must be provided with a 50 mm drain valve and drain pipe. A pressure gauge must be fitted at a point above the seating of the tail-end valve. A subsidiary stop valve may be fitted below the tail-end valve, providing it is of the interlocking key type and in a conspicuous position. When the valve is temporarily closed the key must be readily visible.

5 Pre-action system

A pre-action system is a combination of a standard sprinkler system and an independent approved system of heat or smoke detectors installed in the same areas as the sprinklers. In general, heat or smoke detectors (see Part 2) operate prior to the sprinklers and so a 'pre-action valve' will open to allow water to flow into the sprinkler pipework before the first sprinkler operates. The sprinkler system pipework is normally charged with air under pressure and is monitored so that an alarm is given on reduction of air pressure.

a. Operation of the pre-action valve

The operation of the pre-action valve controlling the water supply is by the approved system of detectors. This allows the sprinkler pipework to become charged with water thus reverting to the wet pipe system. This is to prevent accidental discharge of water from pipework or sprinklers that have suffered mechanical damage. The pre-action valve can also be operated independently by a sprinkler releasing air from the sprinkler pipework, which means that the operation of the sprinkler system is not affected by any failure in the detector system.

The object of this system is to obtain an earlier discharge of water from sprinklers on a dry pipe system.

The maximum number of sprinklers controlled by a pre-action valve, whether in heated or unheated buildings is 500 for extra light hazard and 1000 for ordinary and extra high hazard systems.

In all pre-action systems, operation of the detection system also automatically operates an alarm.

b. Re-cycling pre-action system

A re-cycling pre-action system is a pre-action system of the type described above, with heat detectors and incorporating a special pre-action flow control valve capable of repeated on/off cycles appropriate to the possible re-development of fire in the protected area. The cycling occurs as a result of the heat detector operation which, acting as an electrical interlock, causes the pre-action flow control valve to open and close. As a safety measure, the re-closing of the flow control valve is delayed for a pre-determined period (usually five minutes) by means of an automatic timer. If, however, the fire should rekindle and reactuate the heat detectors, the flow control valve is re-opened without delay and water will again flow from the opened sprinklers.

The objects of the re-cycling pre-action system are:

(i)   to restrict water damage after a fire has been extinguished;

(ii) to avoid water damage caused by accidental mechanical damage to the system pipework or sprinklers;

(iii) to obviate the need to close the main stop valve when replacing sprinklers or affecting modifications to the system pipework.

The heat detectors used for the system must be spaced not more than 12 metres apart and not more than 6 metres from the walls. The maximum number of sprinklers controlled by a pre-action flow control valve, whether in heated or unheated buildings, is 1000. The sprinklers should be installed in the upright position, but where the building is adequately heated they may be installed in the pendent position.

c. Individual on/off sprinkler

An individual on/off sprinkler (Fig. 3.5) using a bi-metal snap disc has been developed and tested. The bi-metal disc expands when heated to a pre-determined temperature and withdraws the pilot valve slightly; this releases some water and allows the piston assembly to drop. Water then passes into the body of the sprinkler and strikes the deflector. When the temperature falls the bi-metal strip returns to its normal position and thus shuts off the sprinkler.

The advantages claimed for this sprinkler are mainly those listed above for the re-cycling pre-action system.

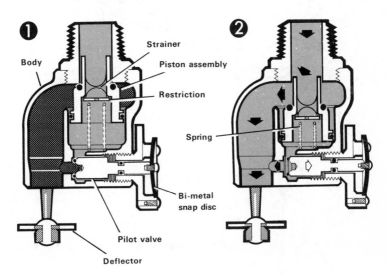

Fig. 3.5 Individual on/off sprinkler (1) Closed position (2) Open position.

6 Deluge system

The deluge system has been designed primarily for special hazards, such as polyester and polyurethane foam-making machines, drying sections of a hardboard plant, firework factories, aircraft hangars, etc. where intensive fires with a very fast rate of fire propagation are expected, and it is desirable to apply water simultaneously over a complete zone in which a fire may originate. This is a system of open sprinklers controlled by a quick-opening valve, operated by approved heat detectors or sprinklers installed in the same area as the open sprinklers.

Quartzoid bulb detectors (Fig. 3.6) are mounted in an independent pipework system containing compressed air, so positioned that wherever a fire may originate, one at least will operate and allow the

compressed air in the pipework to escape. This causes a rapid fall in
pressure on the diaphragm in the automatic deluge valve, to which

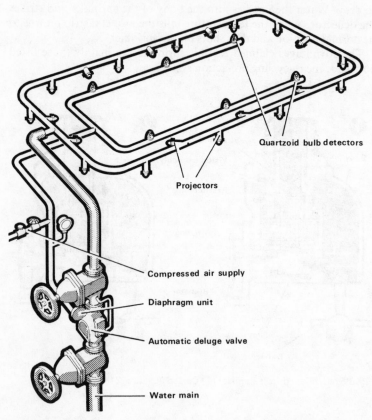

Fig. 3.6 Diagram showing a deluge system.

both systems of pipework are connected. The movement of the
diaphragm causes the deluge valve to open and water to discharge
through the projectors.

Chapter 4
Automatic sprinklers: controls, gauges and alarms

1 Stop valves

Typical layouts for wet and alternate wet and dry pipe systems have already been given. The main stop valve, which is fitted to all installations, enables the water to be cut off after the fire has been extinguished in order to reduce water damage and to permit the actuated heads to be removed and replaced by new ones. The main stop valve is of the gate valve type, operated by a hand wheel. All stop valves must be right-handed (i.e. they must be shut by rotating clockwise), and their hand wheels must be marked to show the direction in which the wheel must be turned to shut the valve. An indication must be fitted which will show whether the valve is open or shut. In order to prevent unauthorised interference and to guard against accidental closure, main stop valves are secured in the fully-open position with a strap which can be cut in case of necessity.

It is a rule of the Fire Offices' Committee that a plan showing the position of the main stop valve or valves must be placed within the building, so that it can be seen easily by firemen or others responding to a call. In addition, a location plate must be fixed on the outside of an external wall, as near to the main stop valve as possible, bearing the following words in raised or other approved letters (Fig. 4.1).

Fig. 4.1 One type of sprinkler location plate.
(It is recommended that the words be white on a black background.)

The main stop valve must be placed close to an entrance to the premises, preferably a main entrance in such a location as to be always readily visible and accessible to authorised persons. It must be secured in the open position by a padlocked or riveted strap, and adequately protected from the action of frost.

In addition to the main stop valve forming part of the installation control valve assembly, each supply to the system is fitted with a stop valve.

Subsidiary stop valves, i.e. above the alarm valve, controlling sections of an installation (for instance, sections of a wet system exposed to frost, such as catwalks, loading places, outside hoists, outside staircases and gangways) which are capable of being shut off and disused during winter months, are only permitted when the area controlled by the secondary stop valve does not exceed 100 m². Suitable drainage facilities must also be provided.

Subsidiary stop valves may also be used on certain sections of a sprinkler installation, such as to facilitate the testing of a dry pipe valve, when a system is permanently on the dry system, or to control sprinklers on a tail-end dry pipe system. The valves are of the interlocking key type. When the valves are closed, the key is readily visible.

2 Non-return valves

The principle upon which a non-return valve works is shown in detail in Fig. 4.2. Water can pass through the valve only in the direction of the arrows by raising the clack valve. Any tendency to cause a flow of water in the reverse direction forces the clack valve on to its seating and so closes the valve.

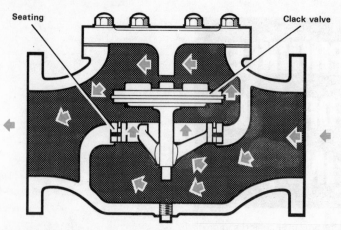

Fig. 4.2 Section through a non-return valve.

Each water supply must be fitted with such a valve, unless there is only a single connection for the installation, when a non-return valve is unnecessary. A few water undertakings insist on the provision of a non-return valve on a single town main connection as an additional safeguard against the return of water from a sprinkler installation into the main. Non-return valves may be placed near the main stop valve, but are most frequently found close to the supply stop valve at the point of entry of the supply into the premises.

Non-return valves are fitted to prevent a reverse flow in the supply system due to the unequal pressures at which they operate. For example, if a town main having a good pressure and an elevated tank are used as water supplies to a sprinkler system, water from the main would, unless a non-return valve were fitted, pass up the supply connecting the tank to the installation and cause it to overflow.

3 Drain valves and test valves

A 40-mm diameter pipe in the case of extra light hazard systems and 50-mm diameter in ordinary and extra high hazard systems is led from the side of the alarm valve in wet installations and from the air chamber of the differential air valve in dry or alternate systems, into a drain. The pipe is fitted with a valve. This drain valve and pipe are used to drain the installation when necessary, and also to carry out pressure and flow tests.

With systems being supplied by town mains, elevated reservoirs and gravity tanks, facilities must be provided to enable 'proving tests' to be carried out at the valves on each installation. This is to verify that the water supply satisfies the requirements of pressure and rates of flow specified for the particular hazard class. The proving tests must be carried out by the installing engineers at the time the system is installed and subsequently as required. The installation drain pipework (Fig. 4.3) is specifically designed to be used for the proving test.

The rate of flow is controlled by manipulation of the drain valve. The actual flow is measured precisely by finding the pressure loss across an orifice plate or some other approved device inserted in the drain pipe. For periodic check testing, a 'standard test orifice' must be used. This is to be left in position permanently. Its purpose is to aid periodic check tests to assess the water supply characteristics by adjustment of the pressure flow characteristics of the drain and test system to a standard form.

4 Pipe drains

In some installations part of the sprinkler piping is below the control valves. In such cases drain cocks are fitted at the lowest parts of the pipes to enable them to be entirely drained of water when required.

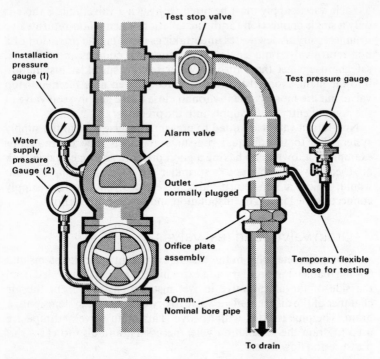

Test stop valve

Installation
pressure
gauge (1)

Test pressure gauge

Water
supply
pressure
Gauge (2)

Alarm valve

Outlet
normally plugged

Orifice plate
assembly

Temporary flexible
hose for testing

40mm.
Nominal bore pipe

To drain

Fig. 4.3 Diagram showing the arrangement of installation proving equipment
(for extra light hazard).

5 Pressure gauges

Every sprinkler system must be fitted with a pressure gauge (Fig.
4.3(1)) above the alarm valve, and this shows the pressure in the
installation (which will be water pressure when the system is on
water, and air pressure when on air). Another gauge (2) must also be
fitted below the alarm and main stop valve, and this indicates the
water supply pressure. When a connection from a town main forms
one of the duplicate water supplies, a gauge (not shown in Fig. 4.3)
must also be fixed on the branch from the main on the town side of
the back-pressure valve. This gauge shows the pressure in the town
main. The reading of this latter gauge may be lower than that of
gauge (2) depending upon the pressure available from the secondary
supply. A supply from a pump is also fitted with a pressure gauge on
the down side of the non-return valve.

The gauges used are normally of the Bourdon tube type and conform to British Standard 1780. There must be means provided to
enable each pressure gauge to be readily removed without interruption of installation water supplies.

The pressure indicated on gauge (1) connected above the alarm valve is sometimes higher than that on gauge (2) below the main stop valve. This is due to the fact that after the system has been charged with water, a rise in pressure in the town main causes the alarm valve to lift and admit pressure to the installation. When, however, the main's pressure falls again, the pressure in the installation is retained by the alarm valve which is, of course, a non-return valve. This difference in pressure sometimes results in a slight delay in the sounding of the alarm gong. When a sprinkler head opens it is necessary for the pressure in the installation to fall below that in the main before the alarm valve opens and allows water to flow to the water turbine of the alarm.

6 Alarm devices

Every installation must be fitted with an approved water motor alarm (Fig. 4.4), located as near the alarm valve as practicable. The

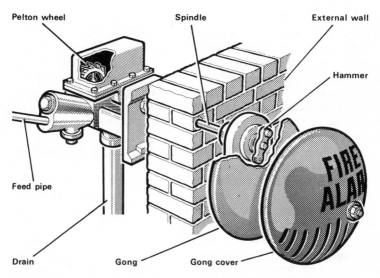

Fig. 4.4 Diagram showing the arrangement of a sprinkler gong and the turbine used to actuate it.

alarm is sounded by a hammer rotated by a small pelton wheel (more generally called a turbine) actuated as water flows into the system. The pelton wheel is fitted inside the building, and is connected by a spindle to the hammer which, with the gong, is positioned outside the building.

The gong is usually placed above and close to the doorway that leads to the main stop valve. Where more installations are fitted to the same building, each has its own gong. Each gong must be numbered in bold figures to correspond with the number painted on the controlling valves of each installation. The flow of water to the turbine may also actuate an electric alarm at a central control point and so give immediate information as to the particular installation that has operated.

There are four causes which may produce a ringing of the alarm gong:

(i)   the opening of a sprinkler head;

(ii) the opening of a drain or test valve;

(iii) damage to any part of the installation which leads to an outflow of water;

(iv) a rise in the pressure of the water being supplied to the installation, thus lifting the alarm valve and allowing water to pass to the turbine operating the gong.

As a precaution against false alarms caused by spasmodic increases of pressure in the town main, most alarm valves contain a small compensating device which permits small quantities of water to pass through to the installation without lifting the clack. The pipe to the water turbine can be fitted with a device known as an 'alarm delay cylinder' which comprises an air bottle fitted with a drain orifice to which the alarm valve connection is led and from which the water turbine is supplied.

If the alarm valve clack lifts momentarily the air bottle is unlikely to fill with water, and thus a false alarm is prevented. When the alarm valve resets, the water drains from the delay cylinder through the drain valve. This device prevents false alarms whilst delaying, to no appreciable extent, the operation of the water turbine when the alarm valve clack is sustained where a sprinkler has actuated, or during a periodical alarm test. Alternatively, a small semi-rotary hand-pump can be fitted to the installation supply pipe and the pressure in the installation can be raised a little above the supply pressure by hand pumping.

In a wet pipe system, the gong may continue to sound after testing owing to a piece of grit becoming lodged under the seat of the alarm valve. Opening the drain valve fully will probably cause the obstruction to be washed away; if not, it may be necessary to close the main stop valve, drain the installation, remove the valve cover and thoroughly clean the alarm valve. The gong may also continue to sound if the alarm valve seat has become scored or pitted so as to allow water to flow continuously.

a. Electrically-operated alarms

Approved water flow alarm switches may be incorporated in the system pipework above the alarm or dry pipe valve to indicate on a central control panel the particular section of the system which is operating. Electric alarm pressure switches, operated by either an increase or fall in pressure, are permitted on a system to operate an auxiliary warning device, but are not accepted as a substitute for the standard water motor alarm device already referred to.

b. Transmission of alarm signals to the fire brigade

Arrangements may be incorporated in the system for the automatic transmission of alarm signals to the fire brigade. Alarm signals may be initiated:

(i)   by a flow of water in the sprinkler system using an electric alarm pressure switch connected to the alarm valve in a similar manner to the sprinkler alarm motor;

(ii) by using water flow alarm switches in the system pipework above the alarm valve;

(iii) by a fall in pressure in the system pipework above the alarm valve.

Pressure switches for transmitting alarm signals to the fire brigade must be of the diaphragm, bellows or Bourdon tube operated type and must be mounted on a vertical branch pipe at least 300 mm long. They must be sufficiently sensitive to operate when only one sprinkler is actuated.

If the connection to the fire brigade is severed at any time as, for example, during hydraulic testing, attention must be drawn automatically to this situation by means of conspicuous duplicated warning lights linked to a buzzer warning. Means must be provided to prevent false alarms occurring with water supplies which are subject to fluctuation in pressure.

The system wiring and power supply must conform to the requirements laid down in British Standard 5839 Pt. I 1980 for 'Electrical Fire Alarms'. A test of:

(i)   the fire brigade connections;

(ii) the circuit between the alarm switch and the control unit; and

(iii) the batteries,

must be made every weekday (except holidays). The first two tests need only be made once a week provided the circuits used are continuously monitored. A notice must be fixed close to the sprinkler test valves of each installation to indicate a direct alarm connection to the fire brigade.

On sprinkler systems where arrangements are incorporated for the automatic transmission of alarm signals to the fire brigade, the arrangements will be regarded as approved by the Fire Offices' Committee if they comply with certain conditions, as follows:

(i) there must be either a connection directly or through a Central Fire Alarm Depot, approved by the Fire Offices' Committee, or through a fire brigade Control with a local authority fire station manned by whole-time personnel, or part-time retained personnel alerted by call-out systems, and so situated as to be capable of providing an attendance at the premises of at least one mobile pumping appliance within the maximum time limit of 10 minutes, or

(ii) a direct connection to a permanently manned watchroom of a private fire brigade consisting of at least one officer and three men always available on the premises and equipped with a power pump (or suitable hydrants conforming to Fire Offices' Committee Rules).

The direct line from the premises whether to the local authority fire station, approved Central Fire Alarm Depot or fire brigade Control, must terminate in a watchroom or control room permanently manned day and night. The use of automatic '999' dialling systems is not approved.

Chapter 5
Automatic sprinklers: sprinkler heads

There are many different designs of sprinkler head but they may be divided into two categories:

(1) those in which the operating medium is fusible solder;

(2) those in which a bulb is ruptured by the expansion of a contained liquid.

1 Fusible solder type

A head of this type which is widely used is shown in Fig. 5.1. The deflector (1), the purpose of which is to spread the water issuing from the orifice, is supported by the two arms of a yoke (2) which screws

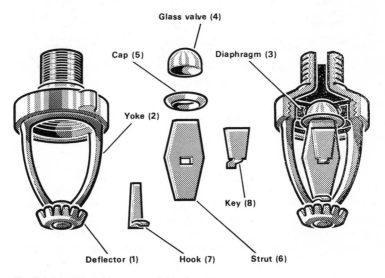

Fig. 5.1 A fusible solder type sprinkler head.

into the body of the sprinkler, the latter being itself screwed to the pipe. Held in place by the yoke is a flexible metal diaphragm (3) with a hole in the centre over which fits a valve (4) of glass or gunmetal. Over the valve is fitted a metal cap (5) and this contains a notch into which the end of the strut (6) is inserted. The strut is supported by two other metal plates: the hook (7), the curved end of which engages the deflector end of the yoke, and the key (8). These three parts are held rigidly together by a special fusible solder and keep the valve cap in position against the pressure in the piping which acts upon the other side of the diaphragm. When the temperature surrounding the head rises to a level at which the solder is heated to its fusing point, the strut, hook and key fly apart owing to the strain under which they are held. The valve cap is released and allows the water an uninterrupted passage to the deflector.

In another type (Fig. 5.2) the metal parts holding the valve cap in place are constructed on the cantilever principle. Here two cantilever members pivoted on one another are connected by a fusible link

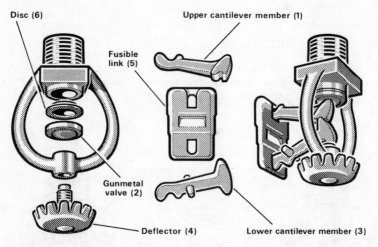

Disc (6) Upper cantilever member (1)

Fusible link (5)

Gunmetal valve (2)

Deflector (4) Lower cantilever member (3)

Fig. 5.2 Another type of fusible solder sprinkler head, which operates on a cantilever principle.

placed outside the arms of the yoke. The upper member (Fig. 5.2(1)) is socketed in the gunmetal valve (2), and the lower member (3) in a slot of the adjustable screw assembly in the deflector boss (4), which enables tension to be given to the cantilever members. When the fusible link (5) melts, the members are thrown clear of the head, additional thrust being given by the pressure of water or air behind the disc (6) which is held in place over the orifice by the valve (2).

A third type of soldered sprinkler head is illustrated in Fig. 5.3. This shows how a soft metal gasket and valve, which form the water-tight joint, are supported by a metal strut, which is retained in position so long as the hemispherical key remains held to the heat collecter by the special solder used for this purpose. When a fire occurs, the temperature of the heat collector and key rises until the

solder melts to release the key. The hook and key then spring outwards and, together with the strut, valve and gasket, are thrown clear
to allow the discharge of water on to the deflector.

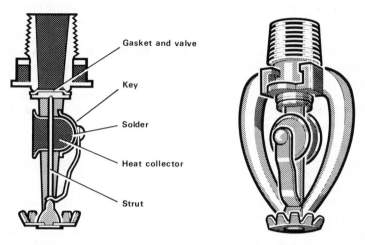

Fig. 5.3 The Mather and Platt 'duraspeed' soldered sprinkler head.

Fusible metal type heads are supplied to operate at various
temperatures, those commonly used being 72°C, 93°C, 141°C,
182°C and 227°C. The fusing temperature of a soldered sprinkler is
stamped on the metal strut; since, however, sprinkler heads may
become uncertain in their operation if the normal room temperature
approaches too closely to the operating temperature, the recommended maximum room temperatures for heads of the above ratings
are as shown in Table 5.

Table 5

Ratings and colours of fusible metal sprinkler heads

Rating of sprinkler	Colour of yoke arm	
68 to 74°C	Uncoloured	The temperature rating chosen
93 to 100°C	White	should be as close as possible to, but not less than 30°C above
141°C	Blue	the highest anticipated temperature conditions
182°C	Yellow	
227°C	Red	

To comply with the rules of the Fire Offices' Committee, sprinkler
heads installed in certain risks—for example, buildings used in

bleach, dye and textile print works, alkali plants, organic fertiliser plants, foundries, pickle and vinegar works, electro-plating and galvanising works, paper mills and tanneries—and in any other premises or portions of premises where corrosive vapours are prevalent, must have approved corrosion resistant coatings (applied by the manufacturer), or must be coated twice with a good quality petroleum jelly. The first coat is to be applied before installation and the second after installation; thereafter the sprinkler heads must be re-coated at periodic intervals as necessary, but only after the removal of the old petroleum jelly and thorough cleaning. In the case of glass bulb type sprinklers, the anti-corrosion treatment is only applied to the body and yoke.

2 Bulb type

In the bulb type head (Fig. 5.4), a small barrel or cylinder made of special glass is used to hold the water valve in place. This bulb is hermetically sealed and contains a quantity of liquid and a small bubble. As the temperature rises, the liquid expands and the size of the bubble decreases until it disappears. A further rise shatters the bulb, breaking it into small pieces so that it cannot obstruct the water flow, and so opens the head. In spite of this ease of fracture, the strength of the bulb is such that it can withstand any pressure applied to the pipe. In a pressure destruction test, it is the metal parts of the head that fail first.

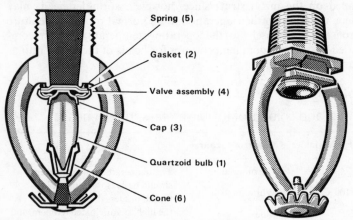

Fig. 5.4 Bulb type sprinkler head.

The gasket (2) is held in position by the bulb (1) which rests at one end upon a hollow in the valve cap (3) which in turn is held in place by a valve assembly (4) and a spring (5) in order that it will throw the parts clear. At the other end the bulb is held in a conical metal cup (6).

By adjusting the composition of the liquid and to some extent the size of the bubble, the bulb type head can be set to operate at any desired temperature. Those most commonly employed are shown in Table 6.

Table 6

Standard bulb filling colours for various ratings of bulb-type sprinkler heads

Sprinkler rating	Colour of bulbs
57°C	Orange
68°C	Red
79°C	Yellow
93°C	Green
141°C	Blue
182°C	Mauve
204 to 260°C	Black

For normal occupancy situations in temperate countries the recommended rating is 68°C. The temperature rating is marked on the deflector of the sprinkler and the liquid filling of the bulb is coloured, a specific colour is used for each operating temperature, as shown in Table 6. The liquid employed is non-freezing and the bulb itself is not subject to corrosion.

3 Sprinkler orifice sizes

Sprinklers are normally manufactured with nominal orifice sizes for the respective hazard class, and these are shown in Table 7. Different

Table 7

Nominal orifice sizes of sprinklers

Nominal size of orifice	Pipe thread	Hazard class
10 mm	10 mm	Extra light only
15 mm	15 mm	Ordinary and extra high only
20 mm	20 mm	Extra high only

Note: See Preface regarding above metric sizes.

pipe threads are also used on the sprinklers and pipework to avoid the possibility of inadvertent interchange between sprinklers of different orifice sizes. The 10 mm and 20 mm sprinklers are also marked in the body or deflector with the orifice size or the letters XLH or EHH as appropriate.

4 Types of sprinkler

Sprinklers must be of approved types and makes. They must not be altered or modified in any way nor have any ornamentation or coatings applied after leaving the manufacturer except corrosion-resisting coatings of petroleum jelly. The following types of sprinkler are acceptable for general use.

a. Conventional pattern

These produce a spherical type of discharge with a proportion of the water thrown upwards to the ceiling. They may be installed upright or pendent.

b. Spray pattern

A hemispherical discharge below the plane of the deflector is produced by this type with little or no water being discharged upwards to the ceiling. An upright version is also available.

c. Ceiling flush pattern

This type (Fig. 5.5(1)) is for use with concealed pipework. The heads are installed pendent with plate or base flush to the ceiling and with the heat-sensitive element below the ceiling line.

   The following types of sprinkler are designed for use in the relevant circumstances.

d. Sidewall pattern

This type (Fig. 5.5(2)) is installed along the walls of a room close to the ceiling and produces a discharge pattern resembling one quarter of a sphere with a proportion discharging on the wall behind the sprinkler. It can be used in positions where condensation dripping from sprinklers and pipework at the ceiling might be a problem, and for aesthetic reasons or for reasons of access where sprinklers at the ceiling are not acceptable.

e. Dry upright pattern

These (Fig. 5.5(4)) are nominally the same as pendent pattern sprinklers. See Fig. 5.5(3).

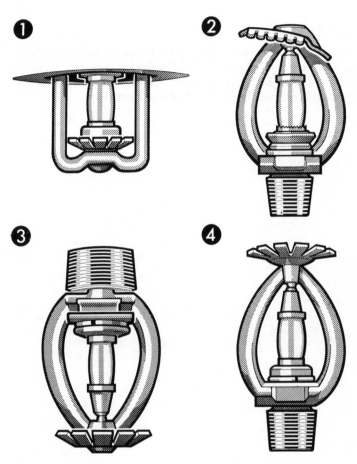

Fig. 5.5 Types of sprinkler : (1) Ceiling flush pattern. (2) Sidewall pattern.
(3) Pendent type. (4) Dry upright type.

5 Life of sprinkler heads

The life of a sprinkler head may be as much as fifty years if it is un-
corroded and has not been subjected to rough treatment or abnormal
temperature. It is, however, advisable to have sample heads removed

and tested when an installation is twenty years old, or earlier if the type of head is no longer made or has proved unsatisfactory in any way.

6 Sprinkler guards

In situations where sprinklers are liable to accidental or mechanical damage, or where otherwise specified by the Fire Insurers, sprinklers must be protected by approved metal guards, although guards must not be used in conjunction with ceiling type sprinklers.

Chapter 6
Automatic sprinklers: general

1 Siting of sprinkler heads

The following definitions are used to differentiate between the various pipework used on a sprinkler installation (Fig. 6.1).

(i) *Main distribution pipes*: main pipes feeding the distribution pipework.

(ii) *Distribution pipes*: pipes directly feeding range pipes.

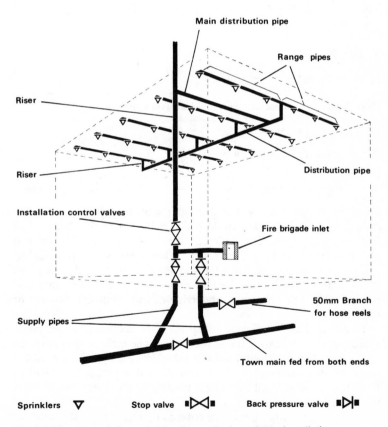

Fig. 6.1 Diagrammatic layout of the pipework of a sprinkler installation.

47

(iii) *Range pipes*: pipes on which the sprinklers are attached either directly or through short arm pipes which do not exceed 300 mm in length.

The number of sprinklers allowed on range pipes depends on the layout and size of pipe used, but does not exceed nine on any one pipe. The number of sprinklers fed by a distribution pipe is also determined by the size of the pipe, with a maximum of 48 heads fed by one distribution pipe. Pipe sizes are determined hydraulically, partly by pre-calculated pipe size tables and partly by hydraulic calculation. The area covered by a sprinkler and the distance between sprinklers on range pipes and adjacent rows of sprinklers is determined by the hazard class of the installation.

2 Area covered by sprinklers

The maximum area covered by a sprinkler in the different classes is shown in Table 8.

Table 8

Maximum area covered by a sprinkler

Hazard class	General	Special risk areas or storage racks
Extra light hazard	21 m²	9 m²
Ordinary hazard	12 m²	9 m²
Extra high hazard	9 m²	7.5 to 10 m²

Sprinkler design ensures that the water shall be deflected on to the ceiling and out in a wide circle which will overlap the distribution from the next head. The deflector should be between 75 mm and 150 mm below ceilings and roofs. Where this is not practicable, sprinklers may be installed at lower levels providing they are not more than 300 mm below the underside of combustible ceilings and roofs or 450 mm below the underside of incombustible ceilings or roofs.

To ensure that the efficiency of sprinkler protection is not lessened, a clear space of at least 500 mm must always be maintained below the sprinkler deflectors throughout the room. For high piled combustible stock, an increased clearance of 1 metre or more must be provided. Roof trusses must at all times be accessible to water discharged from the sprinklers.

All parts of a building must be covered by sprinklers, otherwise fire can develop undetected for a period and become too large for the system to deal with effectively. Any roof space or floor space exceeding 800 mm in depth must be sprinkler protected. Where holes are cut in floors to take machinery drives, conveyors, chutes and other vertical openings such as hoists, lifts and elevators, it is important that a sprinkler is sited above the opening on the upper floor in order that vertical spread of fire does not take place without early detection.

3 Multiple controls

Heat sensitive sealed valve control outlets (Fig. 6.2) are used when it is desired to operate small groups of sprayers simultaneously—hence the term multiple control.

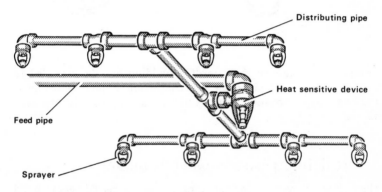

Fig. 6.2 Diagram showing a multiple control system.

The heat sensitive device will be a glass bulb or a soldered link or lever. When this fuses water is delivered to open sprayers which cover the protected area. An example of a control is shown in Fig. 6.3(1) and an open sprayer in Fig. 6.3(2).

4 Extent of a sprinkler system

Where a sprinkler system is installed, it must cover the whole building, except where the omission of sprinklers is specifically allowed as an exception under the rules. Every building communicating directly or indirectly with or adjoining the sprinklered building without separating walls must be sprinklered throughout unless it is one of the permitted exceptions and the separation is a separating wall with openings protected by fire-resisting doors or fire-resisting shutters. Certain detached buildings within a specified distance of the sprinklered building which are considered to present an exposure hazard should also be protected by sprinklers. Alternatively the

c

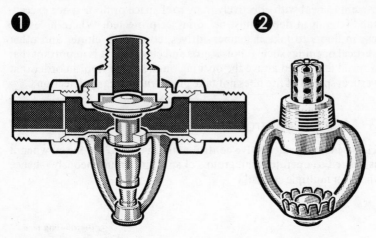

Fig. 6.3 (1) An automatic control. (2) An open sprayer.

sprinkler protection in the protected building may be extended to provide external sprinkler protection over window and door openings and over any combustible sections of the wall opposite the exposure hazard.

5 Fire fighting in a sprinklered building

The following are the principal points a fireman should bear in mind when fighting a fire in a sprinklered building:

(i) On arrival at a fire in a sprinklered building, a member of the crew should immediately be sent to the main stop valve so that:

(a) he can open the valve if he finds it closed, and

(b) he can ensure that the valve is not closed except on the express instructions of the officer in charge.

Many so-called sprinkler failures have been due to premature closing of the main stop valve. A head opens and apparently extinguishes the fire, the water supply is cut off in order to prevent water damage and fire which has continued to smoulder in a hidden place later bursts out again. The premises being deprived of sprinkler protection, the fire grows to large proportions, possibly opening a number of heads. Should the valve then be re-opened the simultaneous discharge of water from these heads causes a drop in pressure and a less effective flow from each head. A sprinkler system is designed to check an incipient fire and not to cope with one that has got away.

(ii) On arrival at an installation where the principal supplies of water can be augmented through a fire brigade inlet, hose should be laid out and a pump connected ready to increase the pressure should a large number of heads have operated.

(iii) It should be remembered that there are many cases where sprinklers will satisfactorily hold the fire which can then be finally extinguished by firemen using hose reels. The sprinklers should not normally be turned off in order that the fire may be fought with jets or spray branches.

(iv) If additional water is needed, it should not be taken from the main supplying the sprinklers unless it is of large size. This main will usually be a branch from a larger town main and pumps should be set into hydrants on the latter, or on a different main. The layout of mains supplying sprinkler installations in their areas should be known by local fire brigade officers.

(v) Although a sprinkler may appear to have extinguished the fire, careful examination of the area involved must be made in order to verify that no trace of fire remains under tables, pipes or stacks of goods.

(vi) When a fire is out and if for any reason it is impossible to turn off the main stop valve immediately and cut off the flow of water to the sprinkler head, water damage can be prevented by securing the female coupling of a length of hose over the head and directing the hose out of a window.

6 The value of sprinklers

Sprinklers have proved their value at many thousands of fires. An analysis of a very large number of fires in sprinkler-protected premises has provided the following statistics:

55 per cent of fires were extinguished by the operation of two or less sprinkler heads.
80 per cent of fires were extinguished by eight or less sprinklers.
90 per cent of fires were extinguished by 18 or less sprinklers.

The very large rebates which are allowed by insurance companies to owners who have installed sprinklers in their buildings are a clear indication of the value of the protection obtained. The rebates vary according to the risk and it is not possible to give any hard and fast rules for approved installations conforming with the standards laid down by the Fire Offices' Committee. The saving is seldom less than 50 per cent of the premium normally charged for the insurance of a corresponding risk without sprinklers.

7 Re-setting of sprinkler systems

Most brigades issue specific orders that following a fire in a sprinklered building, the occupiers are responsible for re-setting the system. This avoids any problems of insurance, etc. should there be a subsequent fire and the system fail to operate.

Chapter 7
Other installations using water

1 Drenchers

While a sprinkler system protects a building from internal fire, drenchers are placed on roofs and over windows and external openings to protect the building from damage by exposure to fire in adjacent premises. The layout of a typical drencher system is shown in Fig. 7.1.

A drencher system is comprised of water-heads somewhat similar to those of sprinklers; these may be sealed or unsealed (open drenchers), but in the latter case the water is turned on manually. In a few instances drenchers may be controlled by quick-opening valves operated by loss of air pressure in a detector line system in a similar manner to high velocity water spray systems (see Section 2).

Drenchers are of three main types:

(a)   Roof drenchers.

(b)   Wall drenchers.

(c)   Window drenchers.

a. Roof drenchers

Roof drenchers (Fig. 7.2(1)) have a deflector rather similar to that of a sprinkler head. From the roof ridge they throw a curtain of water upwards which then runs down the roof. All parts of the roof and any skylights, windows or other openings must be protected.

b. Wall or curtain drenchers

Wall or curtain drenchers (Fig. 7.2(2)) throw water to one side only of the outlet in the form of a flat curtain over those openings or portions of a building most likely to admit fire. In order to cover all combustible portions of a wall, it is the usual practice to put a line of drenchers just below the eaves if these contain flammable material, and to fit every window or opening on the top two storeys with a drencher. Those below this level, except the ground floor and basement, are fitted on every alternate storey.

The drenchers must be fitted so that the streams form a water curtain which must come in contact with the window 600 mm from

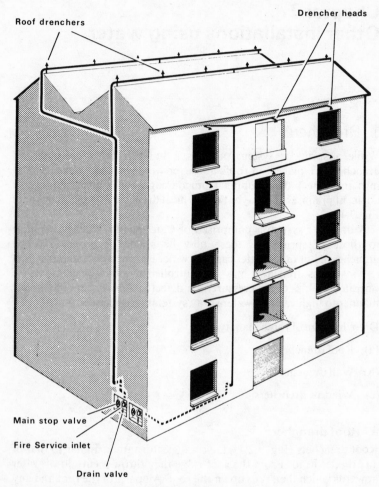

Roof drenchers

Drencher heads

Main stop valve

Fire Service inlet

Drain valve

Fig. 7.1 Diagram showing a typical drencher system.

the top. A special use for this type of drencher is on the stage side of a theatre proscenium arch to protect the safety curtain.

c. Window drenchers

As their name implies, window drenchers (Fig. 7.2(3)) are used to protect window openings. They are placed horizontally level with the top of the window, with the deflector 100 mm from the surface of the wall providing a curtain of water to protect the glass. From the tail of the deflector, a jet is thrown inwards on to the glass near the top of the window, while two streams are directed at an angle of 45 degrees to the lower corners.

d. Water supplies

The installation should be connected to a nominally unlimited water supply with a pressure sufficient to give at least 0.34 bar at the level of the highest drencher with the 50-mm drain valve fully open.

A fire brigade inlet should be provided on the basis of one connection for installations of 55 heads and under, and two connections for installations of over 55 heads. These inlets should be fitted with a non-return valve as should the normal supply pipe.

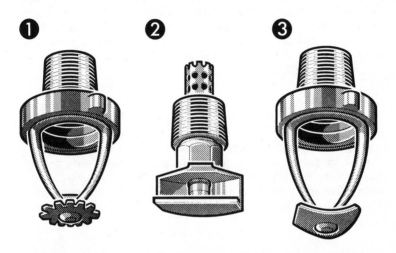

Fig. 7.2 Types of drencher. (1) Roof drencher. (2) Wall or curtain drencher. (3) Window drencher.

e. Valves

The controlling valves must be located in accessible positions on or near ground level and away from fire risk of the exposing hazard. Protection from frost for the supply pipe and valves is essential. A padlocked or riveted strap must be used to secure the valves in the appropriate position. The position of each valve and the drenchers it controls must be clearly indicated by a wall plate. Not more than 72 drenchers may be controlled by a single controlling valve.

f. Spacing of drencher heads

Drenchers fitted on the top row below the eaves and those on the apex of the roof, must have maximum horizontal spacing of 2.5 metres. Windows or other openings, or combustible materials in walls exceeding 2.5 m in width must be protected by two or more drenchers not more than 2.5 m apart, and not more than 1.25 m from the window jambs. Windows separated by not more than 600 mm of incombustible material may be treated as one window. Not more than 12 drenchers may be fixed on any horizontal line of pipe, and not more than six on one side of the vertical feedpipe.

g. Discharge

Drenchers may be either open or sealed. Open drenchers are operated simultaneously by the opening of the main valve, while the sealed type are individually actuated in the same way as a sprinkler head. Sealed drenchers differ little from sprinkler heads except in the shape of the deflector plate. They normally operate on the alternate system, and are more economical in the use of water than open drenchers, since only those heads operate which are required, and the pressure in consequence is maintained more efficiently. Multiple control layouts may, however, be found.

h. Drainage

All pipes and fittings above the controlling valves must be so arranged that the water can be drained away. A 20-mm drain tap and pipe must be fitted immediately above each controlling valve.

In an open drencher system, the drain taps must always be kept open except when the drenchers are in operation. A full-way 50-mm waste valve and pipe must also be installed below the controlling valve or valves, so that the running pressure tests can be carried out at any time.

2 Water-spray projector systems

a. Extinction of oil fires by water

When water is used as the sole means of extinction of oil fires, it is normally applied by means of specially installed fixed fire-fighting equipment closely resembling a sprinkler system.

Precise information as to the way in which burning oil is extinguished is still incomplete, but three main factors are known to be involved (see the *Manual, Book 1, 'Elements of combustion and extinction'*). These are:

(i) cooling;

(ii) dilution of oxygen supplies, and

(iii) dilution (or removal) of the liquid (fuel).

(1) Cooling

Oil burns as a vapour distilling from the surface of the liquid involved in fire. Cooling of the liquid reduces the rate of vaporisation and consequently the rate at which fuel can reach the fire. When water is applied to the burning surface, the oil is cooled by contact with it, the heat absorbed by the water raises the temperature and converts part at least into steam. The latent heat of vaporisation of water (2260 kJ/kg) is such that it is of little importance whether the water projected on to the oil is hot or cold—the cooling effect is caused primarily by its conversion to steam. When water strikes the hot surface of the oil considerable disturbance is caused and the underlying cool oil is mixed with the hot oil which is thereby cooled, thus again reducing the rate of vapour formation.

(2) Dilution of oxygen supplies

The steam formed by the vaporisation of the applied water displaces air from the zone of combustion and thus tends to smother the fire. Furthermore, in water-spray projector systems, the whole of the probable fire area is surrounded by projectors, all of which come into operation on an outbreak of fire. The steam generated, together with the products of combustion seeking to escape from the fire, tend to be driven back into the zone of combustion, and thus still further reduce the oxygen available for combustion.

(3) Dilution of the liquid

If a flammable liquid which will mix with water is progressively diluted, a stage will be reached where so much water is present that the liquid will no longer burn. Petroleum oils, however, cannot mix with water but under certain conditions are capable of forming an emulsion which may consist either of globules of oil suspended in water, or globules of water suspended in oil. The nature of emulsion varies widely, as does its stability; for instance, an emulsion will only last in spirit, such as petrol, whilst it is being formed, whereas in heavy oils it may take several hours to break down. The formation of an emulsion demands energy which must be provided by the water striking the surface of the oil, thus high velocity is required to give high energy to the water drops. Some of the energy may also come from the heat content of the hot oil. This, in evaporating some of the water supplied, causes turbulence which emulsifies the rest. The flammability of an oil-in-water emulsion (that is one in which the drops of oil are surrounded by water) is low because the heat from the fire must pass through the envelope of water surrounding each drop of oil before the latter can be vaporised and add its fuel to the fire.

The relative importance of each of these three factors in the extinction of an oil fire varies considerably, but all three undoubtedly play a part in the operation of a water-spray projector system.

b. Types of system

There are two basic types of water-spray systems installed as fixed equipment. One of these is used to extinguish fires and usually referred to as a 'water-spray projector system'; the other is used to provide protection to plant, equipment and to prevent explosions, and is usually referred to as a 'water-spray protector system'.

c. High velocity system

This system applies water in the form of a conical spray consisting of droplets of water travelling at high velocity; the three principles of extinguishment are employed, namely, emulsification, cooling and smothering.

The high velocity system is used on fires involving medium and heavy oils or similar flammable liquids. Droplets of water travelling at high velocity bombard the surface of the oil to form an emulsion of oil and water that will not support combustion. The effect of this emulsion is to convert a flammable liquid into one that will not burn. The emulsion then formed is unstable and after the water has been shut off, the oil will begin to separate from the water. The length of time that this takes depends primarily on the viscosity of the oil, the higher the viscosity, the longer it will take. The addition of the water to the burning oil also cools it and reduces the rate of vaporisation.

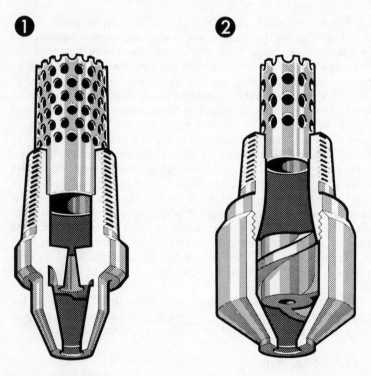

Fig. 7.3 High velocity water-spray projectors. (1) Mather and Platt type. (2) Atlas type.

Thirdly, whilst the water droplets are passing through the flame zone, some of the water is turned into steam, diluting the oxygen feeding the fire thus in effect smothering it.

(1) Projectors

The conical spray of water, consisting of droplets travelling at high velocity, is discharged through specially designed high velocity projectors (Fig. 7.3). These are made in various sizes and are designed to give an even distribution of water over the area covered. The different sizes give a combination of differing flow rates and angles. The equipment is equally suitable for indoor or outdoor use because the pipework can be so designed that no water enters the installation until a fire is detected. The risk of water freezing in the pipework is, therefore, eliminated.

(2) Methods of operation

High velocity water-spray projector systems can be either automatic or manual in operation or, in some cases, manual only. Manual control is usually by hand-operated valves placed outside the probable fire zone, or by valves with remote control from one or more points. There are two main forms of automatic operation.

The glass bulb automatic control (Fig. 7.4) coupled to a small

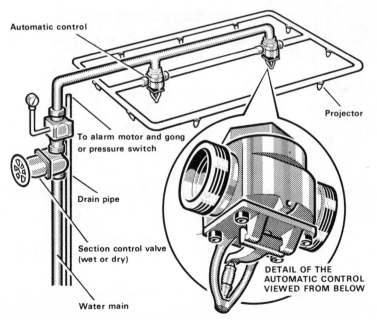

Fig. 7.4 Illustration of a water-spray projector system. (inset) detail of the automatic control from below.

group of projectors, is used in situations where fires in their incipient stages are likely to be small. The projectors are arranged in small groups to cover the risk, each group being connected by pipework to a control (shown inset in Fig. 7.4). When fire causes a control to operate, water is discharged simultaneously through the projectors in the group. When this type of equipment is installed in situations where the temperature may fall below freezing point, the pipework between the controlling valves and the automatic control is charged with compressed air and the system functions in a similar way to a dry sprinkler installation. Where fires are likely to be larger or to spread rapidly over an extended area, a larger number of projectors are designed to operate simultaneously.

A typical application of this method of control is illustrated in Fig. 7.5. Projectors mounted on empty pipework command the whole of the exterior of the transformer and its conservation tank, and also the floor area around the transformer (Plate 3). Glass bulb

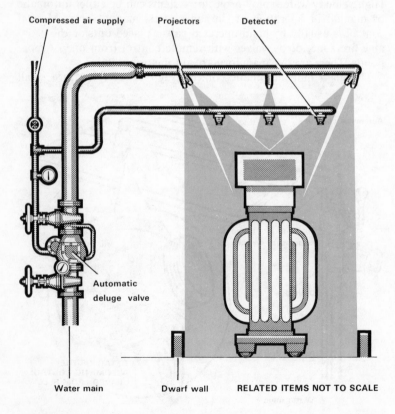

Fig. 7.5 Diagram showing the arrangement of the projectors to protect a transformer.

detectors, mounted on independent pipework containing compressed air are so positioned that wherever a fire may originate, one at least will operate and allow the compressed air in the pipework to escape. The escaping compressed air causes a rapid fall in pressure on the diaphragm in the automatic deluge valve, to which both systems of pipework are connected. The movement of the diaphragm causes the deluge valve to open and water to discharge through the projectors.

(3) Alarms

An alarm is a normal part of a water-spray projector system. It is usually of a type very similar to that used in a sprinkler system, i.e. a loud sounding gong operated by a water motor which is driven by a small flow of water diverted at the installation controlling valves when open. In addition, an electrical alarm may be provided to give warning at some control point of the outbreak of fire and its location.

(4) General

Combined high velocity systems and sprinkler protection may be used in some industrial processes which involve the use of flammable liquids. A glass bulb control forms the fire detecting element and automatic valve for a group of projectors and open sprinklers of a special type which are designed to distribute the water discharge over a wide ceiling area. When the control operates, water is discharged from the projectors on to the burning liquid and from the sprinklers on to the ceiling and adjacent walls.

d. Medium velocity systems

When a fire occurs this system applies water in finely divided drop-lets travelling at medium velocity; it gives protection to tanks, structures and factory equipment by cooling, by controlled burning of flammable liquids and by dilution of explosive gases. Cooling is achieved by the water flowing over the external surface of the exposed vessel and supporting structure, thus reducing their temperature and preventing absorption of heat. Protection by controlled burning is obtained in three ways; firstly by directly cooling the surface of the liquid, thus reducing the rate of vaporisation; secondly by producing steam which dilutes the air and vapour feeding the fire, and thirdly by introducing droplets into the flame thus cooling it and reducing the transfer of heat back to the liquid surface.

When highly flammable gases leak from their containers to form a mixture with air, a critical mixture will form so that any source of ignition may cause an explosion or fire. If the spray system is operated when a leakage has been detected and before fire has started, it produces air turbulence which promotes quicker dilution of the gases by air and water vapour. Fire can be prevented by employ-ing this method to produce quickly a mixture which is too weak to

61

burn. Even if a fire occurs, then the spray system may prevent a dangerous increase of pressure inside the containing vessels and protect the supporting structures against failure caused by high temperatures.

Medium velocity systems are very similar in operation and layout to the high velocity systems previously described. The sprayers discharge a cone of water spray consisting of medium-size droplets of water with a range of different sizes and discharge angles. In most installations the system can be discharged automatically and manually, although some systems may be found which only operate manually. There are three main forms of automatic operation: the first of these is the glass bulb sealed sprayer, very similar to the sprinkler head. The second method, used where a group of sprayers are required to operate simultaneously, is an automatic control as used in the high velocity system, and the third is by the use of two systems of pipework using the automatic deluge valve.

3 Systems using steam

Steam, the oldest of the smothering agents, is not now widely used except in ships' holds (see the *Manual, Part 7, 'Fireboats and ship fires'*—Book 4 in the new format), though it is found occasionally in industry—particularly for the protection of flammable liquids. To be immediately effective, steam must be directed on to the fire in such a way that it blankets the fire. When used for space flooding, it will take considerably longer to be effective because in the early stages of discharge the steam condenses until the whole of the protected space has heated up.

Except when steam from a hand-held type of branch is being used, it is necessary for the space protected to be reasonably airtight. Fixed piping is generally used to connect the boiler with the nozzle arranged to direct the steam on to the risk, it being usual to provide a main valve, either itself designed to open slowly or else fitted with a bypass which must first be opened. The purpose of this precaution is to give employees working in the area warning that steam is being used and to leave the area, whilst also protecting the pipe against severe water hammer. It is not uncommon to locate the valves outside the protected compartment, so that the steam can be turned on without danger to the operator. In some installations, a sprinkler-type layout with fusible heads is used, water being kept in the pipes between the steam and the heads in order to avoid condensation and to prevent the steam from actuating the sprinkler.

Manual steam jet systems, consisting of flexible tubing connected to pipework and fitted with a branch, are frequently found, the control valve for the branch usually being fitted where the tubing leaves the main pipe.

Steam may be used to protect the following risks:

(i)   ships' holds (dependent on cargo);

(ii) flammable liquid users (benzol plants, refineries, dry cleaners, etc.);

(iii) oil quenching tanks, driers, waterproofing processes.

4 Rising mains

A rising main (Fig. 7.6) consists essentially of a pipe installed vertically in a building with a fire service connection or booster pump at the lower end and outlets at various levels throughout the building, (see Plate 4).

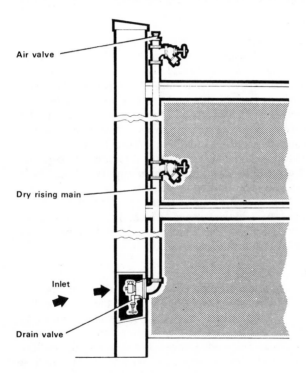

Air valve

Dry rising main

Inlet

Drain valve

Fig. 7.6 Diagram showing the salient features of a dry rising fire main.

There are two types of rising main:

(i)   wet risers;

(ii) dry risers.

Both wet and dry risers have hydrant outlets (sometimes known as landing valves) at various floor levels. In some buildings a system of internal private hydrants is fitted and whilst this system is not strictly speaking a rising main, it operates on similar principles and for all practical purposes may be treated as being the same.

The outlet valves of these hydrants are usually sealed with a wire and lead seal by the water authority to prevent them from being used for purposes other than fire fighting. The outlets are mostly of the wheel-operated type opening anti-clockwise; the direction of opening, however, is always indicated either on the wheel itself or on a plate fitted between the wheel and the locking nut.

Hose may be provided by the occupier for use with risers or internal hydrants, but the modern tendency is to provide small diameter hose reel hose which is more manageable by untrained persons making an initial attack on a fire. (see Plate 5).

a. Wet risers

A wet riser is a pipe kept permanently charged with water which is then immediately available for use on any floor in a building at which a hydrant (or landing valve) is provided. The riser is connected to a town main of suitable capacity with a shut-off control valve installed. If the building height is such that the pressure in the main is insufficient to supply four 13 mm jets at 2.5 bars at the highest outlet, booster pumps are necessary at suitable levels to ensure the maintenance of the required pressure and flow. Where these pumps are employed, the landing valves must be fitted with a pressure regulator to ensure that the pressure head against the pumps (which can be in excess of 20 bars), is not transmitted to the hose.

A similar function to that of a wet riser is performed by what is technically known as a 'down-comer' which, like a wet riser, is constructed of vertical piping, but which is supplied with water from a tank in the roof or at intermediate levels.

b. Dry risers

A dry riser is simply a vertical pipe which is normally kept empty of water, fitted with outlets at various floor levels in the building. It is not connected to a water supply, but is charged when required by means of fire service pumps. In effect, it is a substitute for a line of hose, over which it has many advantages. It enables an upper floor level fire to be attacked by the fire brigade with a line of standard hose without the loss of time entailed in having to lay hose up through the building from the street. It also has a considerably greater capacity than 70-mm hose and also obviates the risk of water damage which might occur if a hose line burst in a part of the building not affected by fire. Further, since an outlet at or near roof level is invariably provided, a riser can be used to feed branches covering a fire in an adjacent building.

A dry riser is charged through inlets at ground level, which are usually housed in external glass-fronted boxes. Each box is normally identified by the words DRY RISING MAIN or DRY RISER CONNECTION painted in red on the glass. Inlets may occasionally be found below pavement level in a box with a cover similar to that used for a hydrant.

An air valve is sometimes fitted at the highest point in the pipe (see Fig. 7.6) to allow the contained air to discharge to atmosphere when the riser is charged with water. Without such a provision, air in the riser might be compressed in the upper part of the pipe and prevent it being fully charged. The air valve, if fitted, is constructed to admit air to the pipe when it is drained after use and so prevent the creation of a partial vacuum, which would result in pockets of water being trapped.

Dry risers are provided with a drain cock fitted beneath the inlets to enable the system to be drained after use. Additionally, where an outlet is fixed at a position below the inlet valves, a further drain valve is fitted at the lowest point of the riser. When emptying a dry riser, it is advisable, if no automatic air valve is fitted, to open the highest outlet to admit air.

c. Type to be used

The type of rising main to be installed in a building is generally determined by the height of the building. In buildings over 18 metres in height, it is recommended that a dry rising fire main should be installed, and in those above 61 metres, a wet riser. As mentioned earlier, booster pumps will be required and a storage tank of about 45 m³ capacity will be needed with a wet riser. The reason why a wet riser must be provided above 61 metres is that brigade pumps will not supply the necessary quantity of water at adequate pressure above this height. For operational reasons, however, the fire service may require dry or wet risers at levels lower than those quoted above.

The outlets from risers should be found in a fire-fighting staircase lobby, in an enclosed staircase forming part of an exit, or in a fire lift enclosure. They may be placed in a glazed cupboard clearly marked FIRE BRIGADE WET MAIN OUTLET or DRY MAIN OUTLET, as the case may be.

In large urban areas, the stealing of wheel valves and other removable parts of outlets presents a problem which if not anticipated by the fire service will render the riser unserviceable in the event of a fire. Brigades are therefore devising their own local plans to overcome this problem. Further, where a dry riser is installed, the possibility of vandalism may make it necessary to check that the wheel valves on each floor are in fact turned off before charging the riser at the inlet. Various methods are being tried in buildings to disguise and/or protect riser outlets from vandals. It is important therefore that the fire brigade is familiar with the siting of, and access to, rising main outlets in buildings within its area.

5 Hose reels

Increasing use is being made of hydraulic hose reels (Fig. 7.7) as the first line of attack against fire. The principal disadvantage of woven hose which is often provided with rising main installations, is that all the hose must be run out before the water can be turned on. This necessitates the presence of more than one person and causes some difficulty if the fire is close to the hydrant. Additionally there are the dangers of an untrained person using a standard size of hose and branch, and the extreme likelihood of excessive water damage. These reasons have led to the increasing use of hydraulic hose reels.

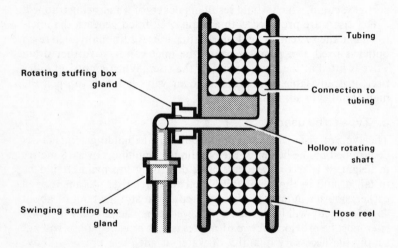

Fig. 7.7 Diagram showing the construction of a typical hydraulic hose reel.

Since only the amount of tubing required needs to be pulled off the reel before the water is turned on (in some cases the water can be turned on before any tubing is run out), only one person is needed to operate it. The comparative lightness and lack of back pressure from the nozzle makes the hose reel a suitable item of equipment for women to use. So many different types of hose reel are in use that it is impractical to describe every variation. In principle, however, the equipment is very similar to the standard hose reel fitted to fire appliances, and no difficulty should be experienced in using any type of hose reel found.

a. Connections

A connection is made to the nearest water supply which may be a branch from a wet riser, a connection via an adaptor to an internal hydrant or a specially installed hose reel main. A stop valve is fitted to control the supply of water to the hose reel, which is usually charged to the nozzle before this valve is closed. The reel itself is mounted on a hollow rotating shaft, to the centre of which water is fed through a stuffing box gland, the tubing being connected to an outlet on this rotating shaft. Rubber tubing of 20 mm or 25 mm in diameter is employed and a light branch with a shut-off nozzle is fitted.

b. Operation

To operate this type of hose reel, all that is necessary is to turn on the valve, and holding the branch, pull off as much tubing as necessary from the reel; the shut-off nozzle is opened when the fire is reached. On some types an automatic valve is fitted to obviate serious delay should the operator fail to turn on the valve before taking the branch to the fire. In one type the action of removing the branch from its holder opens the valve; in another the valve is automatically turned on by the rotation of the drum after a few turns of tubing have been pulled off. To ensure that the tubing pays out easily without kinking or fouling, some form of metal guide is provided, or alternatively, the whole reel swings in the direction in which the tubing is being unreeled. Hose reels are sometimes provided with a fixed metal cover to prevent the collection of dust and to protect the rubber tubing from exposure to light which in time causes deterioration of the rubber.

6 Private hydrants

Private hydrants are often installed in premises with extensive yards, sidings, storage areas, etc. where the nearest statutory hydrant is a considerable distance from the risk, or where the nature of the risk requires large quantities of water to be immediately to hand.

a. Connections

These hydrants may be connected to the service main to the premises, if this is of large enough capacity, to a separate branch from the town main, to a ring main which is connected to the town main at two points or, occasionally, by a single connection.

Ring mains are also installed without any connection to town mains, being supplied from private water supplies such as overhead tanks, reservoirs, lakes, canals, etc. Some premises with a supply from lakes, canals, etc. may also use the town main as a supplementary or primary supply in a fire situation. In this event, the arrangement of valves in the system must ensure that there can be no possibility of contamination of the town main.

A ring main installation has many obvious advantages, the most important of which is that any hydrant is fed by both arms of the ring and that, since a division valve is fitted in both connections with the town main or other water supply and, sometimes, at intermediate points, it may be possible to isolate a damaged section and thus allow a portion of the ring main to remain in action. Where premises are equipped with a sprinkler system as well as private hydrants, separate branches should be provided for each.

b. Hydrant markings

Increasing use is being made of the standard hydrant indicator plate (see the *Manual, Book 7, 'Hydraulics and water supplies'*) to mark the position of private hydrants, although various individual markings may still be found. The hydrants themselves are of various patterns, the most common being the standard underground hydrant; less common are pillar hydrants and wall hydrants.

c. Outlets

The outlets of private hydrants usually conform to British Standard 750, although other types may be found. Where private hydrants are non-standard, adaptors should be provided at the premises to enable fire brigade equipment to be utilised.

d. By-pass valves

As private mains usually supply the domestic needs of the premises, they are almost always fitted with a water meter so that the water undertaking can record the consumption. Where water is fed into industrial premises for business purposes through a meter, it is common practice for a by-pass to be fitted. If the water on the factory side of the meter is required for fire fighting, the meter can be by-passed by opening the by-pass valve, thus eliminating frictional resistance through the meter. In addition, the water used for fire fighting does not register on the meter. The location of the valve controlling a meter by-pass should be indicated by a standard by-pass indicator plate (see the *Manual, Book 7, 'Hydraulics and water supplies'*). The valve is usually wire-locked in the closed position and when a hydrant is used for fire fighting, the valve should be opened fully to enable the maximum flow to be obtained.

Chapter 8
Extinguishing systems not using water

This chapter deals with the equipment and fittings installed to protect buildings by means other than the use of water. The fireman needs to be familiar with the media used in these installations since it will be necessary for him to carry out a thorough investigation after an installation has been actuated. This investigation will be necessary in order to verify that the fire has been extinguished and that no 'bull's eyes' or pockets of fire remain.

The installations described include those which use foam, carbon dioxide and other vaporising liquids. A brief mention is also made of dry powder and inert gas equipment.

1 Foam installations (LX)

a. Pump-operated mechanical foam installation

This type (Fig. 8.1) comprises a foam concentrate tank outside the area to be protected, the capacity being dependent on the area involved. The tank has a water supply and an inductor fitted to it.

The water control valve is opened until the required amount of water (measured by the water meter) is flowing into the tank. The 'venturi effect' created in the inductor draws the resultant mixture of foam concentrate and water from the tank through the non-return valve. The foam solution is then delivered to foam generators within the protected area, where foam is immediately formed and conveyed to the spreaders or pourers.

b. Self-contained pressurised type

This type is used where suitable pumps or water supplies are not available. The system (Fig. 8.2) comprises a water storage tank and a foam concentrate storage tank, the capacity of each being dependent on the area to be protected. One or more carbon dioxide cylinders are fitted to expel the water from the storage tank. An inductor unit is fitted adjacent to the tanks and two pipes are led from the unit to the

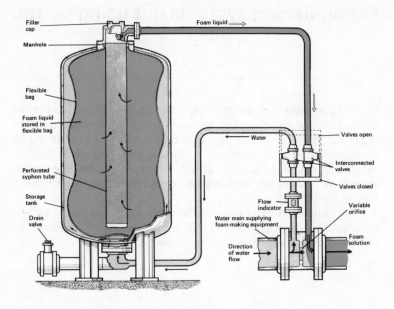

Fig. 8.1 Mechanical foam installation : pump-operated type.

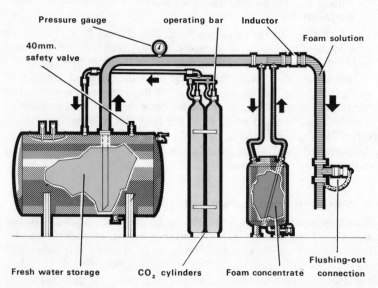

Fig. 8.2 Mechanical foam installation : self-contained pressurised type.

foam concentrate tank; the high pressure side leads to the top of the tank and the low pressure side to the internal siphon tube. When the CO_2 is released from the cylinders it expels the water from the storage tank through the inductor, the right amount of concentrate being drawn from the concentrate tank into the water stream. The foam solution is then delivered to the generators in the protected area where foam is formed and conveyed to the spreaders and pourers.

c. Pre-mixed foam installations

A pre-mixed foam installation (Fig. 8.3) comprises a cylindrical storage tank, designed for a maximum working pressure of about 10 bars, which is filled with a foam solution (i.e. foam concentrate and water). The capacity of the tank is determined by the quantity and depth of foam converage required. The tank is fitted with an inlet connection from a carbon dioxide gas cylinder (or cylinders) of appropriate capacity, having a disc-closure valve and a lever-operated piercing head. The rate of discharge of the CO_2 gas in the event of fire is controlled so that a continuous pressure will be maintained within the storage tank, giving a constant rate-of-flow foam.

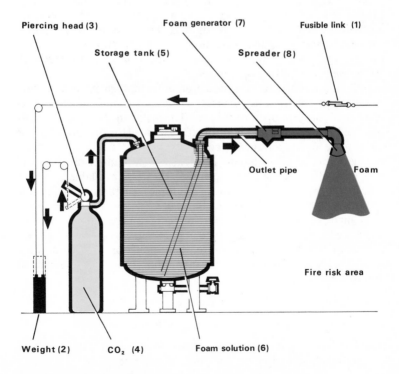

Fig. 8.3 A pre-mixed foam installation.

An outbreak of fire will cause the fusible link (Fig. 8.3(1)) to break and allow the weight (2) to fall. This raises the lever of the piercing head (3) thus releasing CO_2 gas from the cylinder (4) into the storage tank (5). The foam solution (6) is forced up the siphon tube and along the outlet pipe to the foam generator (7). The foam is distributed by perforated pipes or spreaders (8) which are arranged to give even or concentrated distribution (e.g. over a boiler front) as required.

If any of the systems described in (a), (b) or (c) above protect more than one area of risk, distribution valves may be included to direct the foam to the required area.

2 High expansion foam installations (HX)

High expansion foam, as used in fixed installations, is a mass of uniform bubbles, each about 10 mm in diameter, having an expansion ratio of approximately 1000 volumes of foam for each volume of solution. One of its principal attributes, therefore. is the ability to produce a large amount of foam from a small amount of water, with a consequent reduction in water damage. Details of the way in which the generators work, and the action to be taken at fires when using this extinguishing medium, are given in the *Manual, Book 3, Part 3, 'Foam and foam-making equipment'*.

In addition to the actual production of foam, high expansion foam installations incorporate devices which automatically close fire-resisting doors and open roof vents. The installations are electrically operated by relays from an automatic fire detector operating on the 'rate of rise' of temperature principle.

The output of an automatic high expansion foam installation will vary depending on the generator used. These are available in a wide output range; in fact, the use of multiple generators can provide systems with a virtually unlimited output, so allowing an assessment to be made of the size and number of generators required to provide adequate foam delivery in any type of building.

If any one detector locates a fire, the installation actuates and the following sequence of events is set in motion. (In practice these occur almost simultaneously.)

(i)   Alarms sound in the affected area.

(ii) A valve opens allowing water to pass to the generator.

(iii) The pump motor is switched on and foam concentrate is injected into the water supply at a pre-determined rate.

(iv) The fan motor (if fitted) is started.

(v) Water gathers in an accumulator, producing pneumatic pressure which opens protective doors on the generator, opens doors covering duct openings in the affected area and sets in motion the mechanism for closing fire-resisting doors and opening roof vents.

3 Foam inlets

In many buildings rooms containing oil fuel, oil-fired boilers or other flammable liquids, are protected by fixed piping through which foam can be pumped. The piping, which is arranged to suit the risk, is run from the room to an appropriate point in the street where it terminates in a fire service inlet (Fig. 8.4) usually protected by a glass panel and marked with the words FOAM INLET (Plate 6), together with an indication of the particular risk involved.

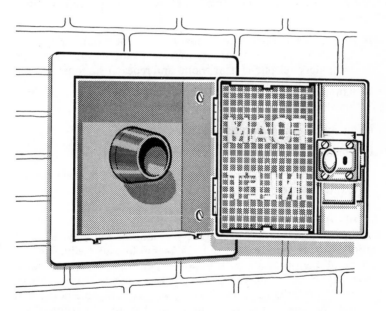

Fig. 8.4 A fire service foam inlet showing a foam inlet adaptor, tapered type, in accordance with British Standard 336.

The inlet pipes are fitted with a foam inlet adaptor, a specification for which is included in British Standard 336. This has a tapered orifice which is suitable for most types of low expansion foam-making branch. This arrangement ensures that foam can be applied where it is required in the early stages of what may be a fierce fire without it being necessary for firemen to enter the compartment.

4 Carbon dioxide installations

a. Application and limitations of carbon dioxide

The use of carbon dioxide installations is confined primarily to hazards which are located inside buildings, or around which protective screens can be erected. Although heavier than air, the gas is comparatively light and it may be dispersed away from the fire if subjected to any appreciable air currents. The gas discharges at low temperature, but this does not produce much cooling effect in the fire area and is never taken into consideration when designing an installation, dilution of the atmosphere being the main extinguishing effect.

Carbon dioxide is not suitable for extinguishing fires involving materials which contain their own oxygen supply, e.g. nitrates, chlorates, reactive metals such as sodium, potassium, magnesium, etc. It has a particular application where delicate equipment or materials are involved and some examples of the types of risk where it can be used satisfactorily are:

(i)   a wide variety of electrical apparatus and electronic equipment, e.g. electrical switchgear, transformers, alternators, electronic computers, telephone relay rooms and repeater stations;

(ii) flammable liquids, e.g. paint stores, paint dip tanks, small spray booths, solvent stores, printing ink;

(iii) chemical laboratories and chemical stores;

(iv) libraries, archives, valuable art stores, record stores, etc.;

(v)   diesel and diesel-electric locomotives, ships' holds, machinery in textile industry.

b. Gas stored in cylinders

The installation consists of a battery of one or more cylinders of carbon dioxide interconnected by a manifold and feeding into a system of high-pressure distribution pipework. Special discharge nozzles are fitted at intervals on the pipework and upon operation of the installation, the gas is discharged, with considerable noise, into the protected space or on to the particular hazard. Operation of the installation can be either automatic or manual by the use of electrical or mechanical equipment.

Where protection is required for more than one compartment or zone, one of the following arrangements is usually found:

(i)   sufficient cylinders may be provided to flood all spaces simultaneously;

(ii) a separate group of cylinders may be provided for each space, in which case they can be interconnected and used as reserves;

(iii) one battery of cylinders may be used to protect two or more spaces (this is termed 'joint protection');

(iv) a reserve bank of cylinders is sometimes found.

c. Gas stored in refrigerated tanks

The gas is stored in a refrigerated tank at a temperature of $-18°C$ and at a pressure of about 20 bars. The tank is connected by suitable pipework to the protected spaces with discharge nozzles strategically sited on the pipework within the space to cover the risk. A number of different risks within the same premises can be protected using a single tank, and tank capacities range from 3 tonnes upwards depending on the number and size of the chambers being covered.

Operation of the system is usually triggered off by the use of a suitable automatic fire detection system. When the system operates, a distribution valve is automatically opened for a predetermined period, allowing sufficient gas to be released to totally flood the protected space, and then automatically closes.

Overriding manual control is incorporated into the design of the system and should re-ignition occur, further charges can be released into the space as required.

d. General considerations

When considering how much gas is required and what type of installation is necessary, the main factors which are given attention are:

(i)   the volume of the space;

(ii) the nature of the hazard;

(iii) whether the hazard is enclosed or not;

(iv) whether fire is likely to spread from one compartment to another;

(v)   the chances of fire occurring in more than one space at the same time.

e. Lock-off devices

Every installation must be provided with means of immobilising the equipment, as it is important that automatic operation should not occur whilst people are in the protected zone. Provision is usually made to:

(i)   'lock-off' the automatic feature only (leaving overriding manual control), and

(ii) completely immobilise the installation.

These devices can usually be operated from a remote position outside the protected area.

f. Indicating and alarm devices

Automatic visual warning, using a system of coloured indicator lights, is usually provided to indicate:

(i)   manual control;

(ii)   automatic control;

(iii) carbon dioxide discharged.

In addition, visible and/or audible warning may be provided to indicate an electrical fault. All indicators may terminate at a central control where necessary, in addition to a warning on site.

g. Other automatic devices

By diverting a small amount of the gas to pressure-operated switches and trip mechanisms it is possible automatically to:

(i)   operate door-closing devices;

(ii)   close openings in ventilating ducts;

(iii) switch off ventilating systems;

(iv)   operate asbestos curtains.

h. General safety precautions

Aisles and routes of exits should be kept clear at all times. Adequate lighting and/or emergency lighting with directional signs to ensure quick staff evacuation may be necessary for large protected chambers. Provision of sufficient alarms within the area that will operate immediately upon detection of fire and at the time of CO_2 discharge. Alternatively, the alarms should sound for a time interval before operation of the CO_2 installation. Operation of automatic door closures should not prevent the door being opened by trapped personnel. Outward-swinging self-closing doors are recommended at exits from the hazardous area.

Warning and instructional signs or notices should be positioned at the entrance to protected fire risks. In most cases where CO_2 is installed, the actual hazard to personnel is rather small, but the hazard will always be greater where the enclosure is large and where carbon dioxide may enter adjacent spaces such as pits and basements.

The extent and type of warning to personnel must be designed to suit the requirements of each particular site. Usually adequate warning notices, bells and indicating lights are provided with an installation. They are put there for the guidance of work people within the vicinity of protected areas. Therefore, it is also recommended that fire brigade personnel should comply with the instructions given on any notices.

Premises fitted with carbon dioxide installations will display a distinctive symbol (Fig. 8.5) as a warning of the presence of concentrated gases.

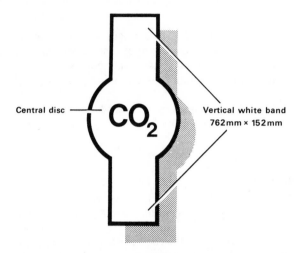

Fig. 8.5 Standard carbon dioxide warning symbol.

5 Vaporising liquid installations

A group of halogenated hydrocarbon extinguishing agents has been developed during recent years and are used in fixed installations. They are:

(i)   bromotrifluoromethane (generally referred to as BTM, freon 1301 or halon 1301);

(ii) bromochlorodifluoromethane (generally referred to as BCF or halon 1211);

(iii) chlorobromomethane (CBM) (this has largely been superseded by BTM and BCF).

These extinguishants have the same cleanliness in operation as carbon dioxide, but are more expensive. They are, however, used in preference to CO_2 for particular types of hazard and equipment, such as:

(i)   gaseous and liquid flammable materials;

(ii) electrical hazards, such as transformers, oil switchgear and circuit breakers;

(iii) engines using petrol and other flammable fuels;

(iv) ordinary combustibles such as paper, wood and textiles;

(v) hazardous solids;

(vi) electronic computers, data processing equipment and control rooms.

Vaporising liquids should not be used to extinguish fires involving chemicals containing their own oxygen supply, such as cellulose nitrate, nor on reactive metals, such as sodium, potassium, magnesium, titanium, zirconium, uranium and plutonium, or on metal hydrides.

Details of the characteristics, uses and hazards of vaporising liquids are detailed in the *Manual, Book 3, Part 2, 'Portable fire extinguishers'*.

a. Fixed installations

Halogenated hydrocarbons are gases at normal temperature and pressure. They are liquefied by compression for storage and although the vapour pressure in some cases is adequate to expel the contents of the storage containers, this pressure decreases with a fall in temperature. It is therefore usual to pressurise the containers by the use of nitrogen.

Each container is equipped with suitably designed valves to retain the agent in its container and capable of discharging the liquid at the required rate. Containers with top-mounted valves have an internal dip tube extending to the bottom of the cylinder to permit discharge of the liquid. When the system operates, the liquid is fed through distribution pipework to specially-designed discharge nozzles which are sited strategically round the risk. Upon discharge the liquid immediately vaporises to form a heavy vapour which achieves very rapid extinction. Two sections of a BTM installation are shown in Plates 7 and 8.

Because of the high efficiency and rapidity of flame knockdown that can be achieved by halogenated hydrocarbon extinguishing agents, they are ideally suitable for use in automatic systems. Any unnecessary delay in the actuation of a system may reduce its effectiveness, because the size of the fire may be increased. This could result in an increase in the concentration of breakdown products. It is for this reason that automatic detection and operation should be used whenever possible. However, it should be recognised that there may be exceptional circumstances in which manual operation is to be preferred. There are two types of system which may be found installed:

(i) total flooding systems;

(ii) local application systems.

A total flooding system consists of a supply of the vaporising liquid arranged to discharge into and fill to the required concentration, an enclosed space or enclosure about the hazard. This system is very similar in layout to the carbon dioxide system (see page 74) and may provide fire protection within rooms, vaults, enclosed machines, ovens, containers, storage tanks and bins. Vaporising liquid total flooding systems will not be used in normally occupied areas in concentrations greater than 7 per cent.

Local application systems may be used to extinguish surface fires in flammable liquids, gases and solids where the hazard is not enclosed. Some examples of hazards that may be successfully protected by local application systems include dip tanks, quench tanks, spray booths and oil-filled electric transformers.

Discharge of the agent may create a light mist in the vicinty of the discharge nozzle, resulting from condensation of moisture in the air, but the mist rarely persists after discharge is completed. Once discharged into an enclosure, it is difficult to detect its presence through normal human senses; in concentrations above about 3 per cent, voice characteristics are changed due to the increased density of the agent/air mixture.

In total flooding systems, the high density of BTM vapour (five times that of air) requires the use of discharge nozzles that will achieve a well-mixed atmosphere in order to avoid local pockets of higher concentration. It is also possible to develop local pockets of higher concentration in pits of low-lying areas adjacent to local application systems. Once mixed into the air, the agent will not settle out.

b. Safety requirements

Safeguards are necessary to prevent injury or death of personnel in areas where the atmosphere may be made hazardous by the discharge or decomposition of vaporising liquids. These may include the following:

(i) Adequate gangways and routes to the exit; these should be kept clear at all times.

(ii) Provision should be made for any necessary additional or emergency lighting and directional signs to ensure quick, safe evacuation.

(iii) The provision of alarms within such areas; these should operate immediately upon the detection of a fire.

(iv) Outward opening self-closing doors should be provided at exits from the hazardous area.

(v) Continuous alarms or a system of coloured lights should be provided at entrances to such areas to indicate that the system has operated.

(vi) Warning and instruction notices should be provided at entrances and inside such areas, to inform personnel that a vaporising liquid system is installed. The notice should contain instructions on the action necessary in the event of the operation of the system.

(vii) Instruction and drills should be carried out to ensure the correct action is taken by personnel within or in the vicinity of such areas when the equipment operates.

(viii) Provision should be made for the prompt ventilation of such areas. Care should be taken to dissipate the hazardous atmosphere and not merely to transfer it to another area.

(ix) Provision of other safeguards that may be warranted in particular circumstances to prevent injury or death.

c. Action by the fire service

When responding to a fire where a total flooding system has operated in a room, the door should not be opened until the officer in charge is satisfied that the fire is out, unless it is necessary to perform a rescue. The system is designed to extinguish surface fires involving flammable liquids or solids, or gas fires. These will be extinguished very quickly, once the required concentration (usually under 5 per cent) is reached. However, if the fire being extinguished is deep seated, then the door should not be opened until sufficient time has elapsed to allow the gas to be effective and the material to cool, so that re-ignition will not occur when the inert atmosphere is dissipated. Before deciding to make an entry to the compartment, the fire brigade officer should have equipment laid out and prepared ready to deal with any fire that might reoccur. The room should be entered only by men wearing breathing apparatus until such time as the area has been well ventilated. When the fire has been extinguished, fans should be switched on and windows opened to rid the area of the decomposed gas and the products of combustion.

In the majority of instances, a fire attacked by the application of vaporising liquid in a fixed installation will be extinguished before the arrival of the fire brigade. Dip tanks, quench tanks, spray booths, etc. when protected by a properly-designed system (one that compensates for any vents or fans which cannot be closed automatically or shut down) will have had sufficient extinguishing agent discharged into them to extinguish the fire. Nevertheless, it is always advisable, regardless of the agent used, to back up any system, whether of local application or total flooding, with suitable extinguishing media in case the system fails to function.

Plate 1. A gravity tank used in the supply of water to a sprinkler system.

Plate 2. A cylindrical steel pressure tank used in the supply of water, in whole or part, to a sprinkler system.

Plate 3. A typical application of an emulsified water projection system.

Plate 4. A rising main showing an outlet at one level of the building.

Plate 5. A rising main in glass fronted box with the hose reel adjacent.

Plate 6. A fire service foam inlet.

Plate 7. Part of a BTM installation showing two discharge nozzles.

Plate 8. A bank of supply cylinders for a BTM system.

Plate 9. In-line sprinklers which can be installed into vertical feed pipes of a high-speed sprinkler system.

Plate 10. Ground level sprinklers protecting the 'Concorde' showing three of the Pyrene GFS 20 pop-up nozzles raised out of their cast iron cylinders to illustrate their operating position. The remaining nozzles are not visible as they lie flush with the hangar floor. The loosely fitting caps can be seen alongside the raised nozzles.

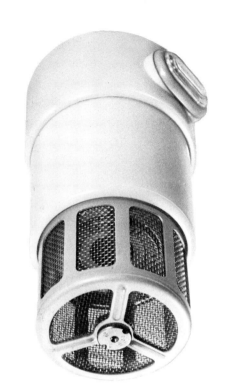

Plate 11. An
ionisation detector
—double chamber
—(approximately
130 mm × 80 mm).

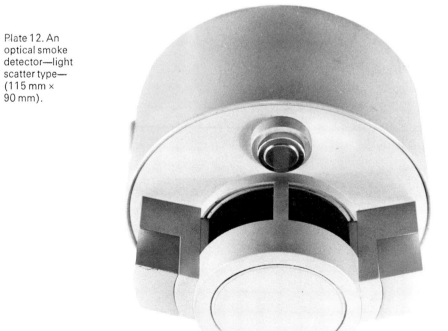

Plate 12. An
optical smoke
detector—light
scatter type—
(115 mm ×
90 mm).

Plate 13. An infra-red radiation detector—(140 mm × 76 mm).

Plate 14. An infra-scan radiation detector—(292 mm × 280 mm).

Plate 15. An ultra-violet detector and amplifier—(detector 178 mm × 127 mm).

Plate 16. A 'Dimac' heat detector—(approximately 203 mm × 76 mm).

Fusible link

Plate 17. A break-link cable heat detector.

Plate 18. A 'Pyrene 30D' heat detector—(63 mm × 57 mm).

Plate 19. A 'Fidela' heat detector—(197 mm × 57 mm).

Plate 20. A May-Oatway Mk 1' heat detector (2.2 metres × 152 mm).

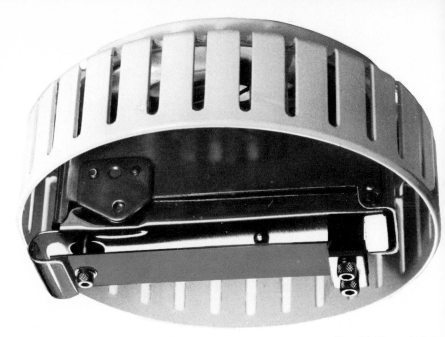

Plate 21. 'Gents 1151' heat detector—(115 mm diameter × 38 mm).

Plate 22. A 'Pyrene' rate-of-rise detector—(61 mm × 57 mm).

Plate 23. A 'Fyrindex'
automatic fire detector—
(90 mm diameter ×
51 mm).

Plate 24. A detector head
used in the Kidde
pneumatic system
(Approx. 115 mm ×
76 mm).

Plate 25. An infra-red beam detector—the units—(250 mm × 150 mm).

Plate 26. An infra-red beam detector—emitter (interior).

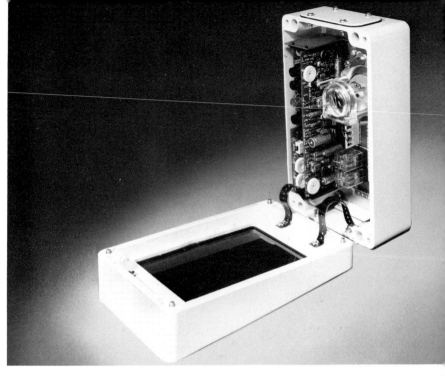

Plate 27. An infra-red beam detector—receiver (interior).

Plate 28. A rotary gong.

Plate 29. A manual call point.

Plate 30. A manual call point—press button type.

Plate 31. A manual call point—with hammer.

Plate 32. A manual call point—key type.

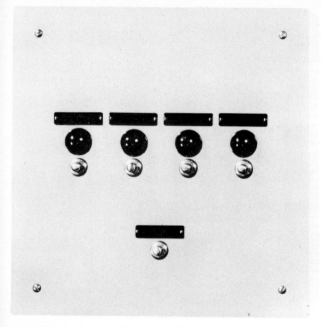

Plate 33. A luminous indicator panel/control unit.

Plate 34. A more sophisticated type of luminous indicator panel/control unit.

Plate 35. Right above : A luminous indicator with building plan adjacent.

Plate 36. Right below : A signal selection unit.

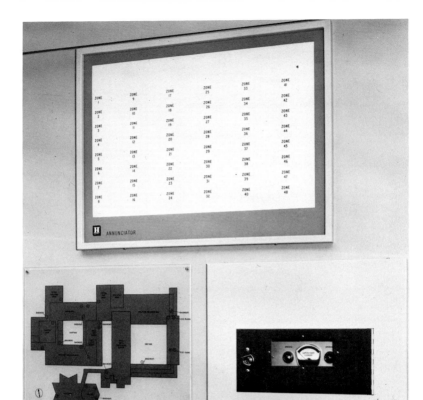

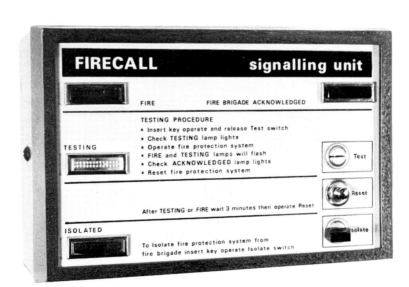

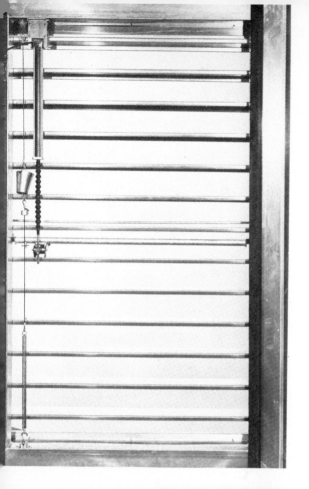

Plate 37. Close up of one type of automatic fire ventilator showing pneumatic ram and stainless steel opening spring (captive until freed by fusible link). Link is hidden by conical shield which prevents sprinkler water cooling the link.

Plate 38. A twin-door roof vent operated by a fusible link.

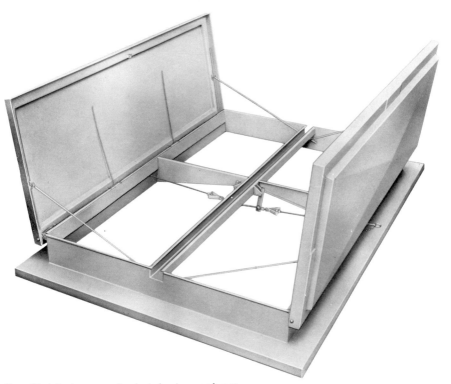

Plate 39. A further example of a twin-door roof vent operated by a fusible link.

Plate 40. Fireman's over-ride control for testing operation of fire vent installation or to open vent in advance of fusing temperature being reached.

Plate 41. Automatic fire
ventilators on the roof of an
automated high-bay warehouse.
(Note—Small inclined rain-
sensing panel on vent in left
foreground.)

Plate 42. The 'Type A' vertical
fire/seal steel curtain fire damper
shown open.

Plate 43. The 'Type A' vertical fire/seal steel curtain fire damper shown closed.

Plate 44. An intumescent damper as seen before a fire.

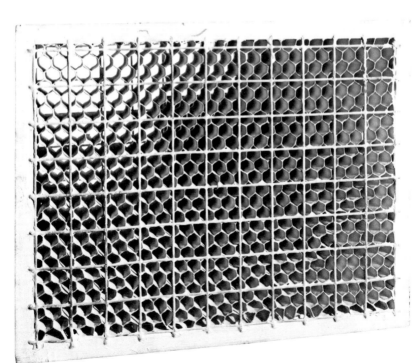

Plate 45. An intumescent damper (same face as in Plate 44) after fire.

Plate 46. The same intumescent damper (as in Plates 44 and 45) showing the effect when fire approaches from the reverse side.

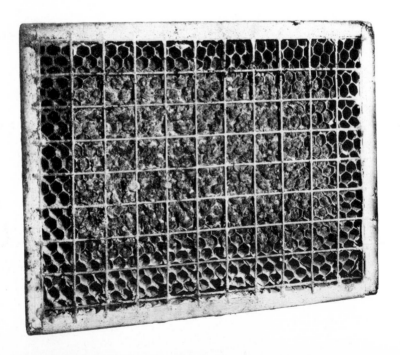

6 Dry powder installations

Dry powder provides a further range of chemical agents available as extinguishing media, and the properties of these are dealt with in the *Manual, Book 3, 'Fire extinguishing equipment'*. In common with vaporising liquids, dry powders offer the advantage of a quick knockdown of fire, but unlike the vaporising liquids, they have negligible toxic effects. A major disadvantage is that they require a lot of clearing up once an installation has operated. Compacting of the powder is also a problem, due to heat or vibration in normal storage and in moist atmospheres; this could present difficulties in the maintenance of the system especially after discharge when compacting could take place in valves, etc. It is claimed, however, and tests seem to bear this out, that the more recently developed powders (e.g. 'Monnex') are free of this problem.

A dry powder installation consists of specially-designed pipework and discharge nozzles covering the protected risk, the pipework being linked to the dry powder containers. When a fire occurs it is necessary to pressurise the powder so that it is forced through the pipework and discharge nozzles. This is usually done with CO_2; a line detector is linked to a lever which when actuated allows the head of a CO_2 cylinder to be pierced (similar to the operation shown in Fig. 8.3). The carbon dioxide thus released pressurises the dry powder and forces it over the protected area. Dry powder installations can normally be operated automatically or manually.

Dry powder can be used on various flammable liquids where they are confined in storage tanks, flammable gases, oil-filled equipment and combustibles where the fire is on the surface. Special powders have also been developed to deal with metal fires (see the *Manual, Part 6C, Practical Firemanship III, Chapter 45, 'Metal Fires'* (Book 15 in the new format).

7 Inert gas installations

Several inert gas systems using incombustible products of diesel oil have been developed. These systems can generate a continuous supply of gas (mostly nitrogen) for several hours so that whilst a fire is being dealt with in one particular space, the gas can also be directed to adjacent spaces to stop it spreading.

The use of this type of installation is mainly confined to the protection of ships' holds and is described in detail in the *Manual, Part 7, 'Fireboats and ship fires'* Book 4 in the new format).

Chapter 9
Installations for special risks

1 High-bay warehouses

The high-bay (or high-racked) warehouse presents a particular type of fire risk because of its size and height and the variety of goods stored in close proximity under one roof. The problem of providing efficient sprinkler systems for these types of building has been the subject of research during recent years, and the Building Research Establishment have issued a 'Current Paper' on 'The rapid extinction of fires in high-racked storages' (See 'Further reading'—Page 181).

In high-bay warehouses, height is a particular factor which increases the difficulty of extinguishing a fire. Ceiling sprinklers, for this reason, are not always effective, hence the insistence in the Fire Offices' Committee Rules on sprinklers at intermediate levels for certain hazard categories. Experiments have been carried out on fires in high-racked storages with sprinklers distributed at intermediate levels within the racking and operated by the usual glass bulb or fusible link. In nearly all these experiments, the fire has spread right through the top of the racking causing considerable fire, smoke and water damage. This is because the sprinklers generally operate after the flame has passed above them, thus making control of the developing fire more difficult.

a. Speed of operation of sprinkler system

While this system is capable of containing a fire, damage could obviously be further restricted if the fire were detected AND suppressed within the slow initial stage of its growth. To achieve this it was concluded that:

(i)   a quick-acting sprinkler was desirable, and

(ii) a zone or group of several sprinkler heads operated together would be a more certain means of controlling a fire than a single head.

In the system which was developed with these points in mind, the protected area is divided into zones (Fig. 9.1) and a line detector is distributed throughout the zone to ensure that wherever the fire starts within that zone it will be detected in its initial stages. The line detector used consists of a pair of steel wires, each insulated with a cellulosic layer, and the two twisted together. Further layers of

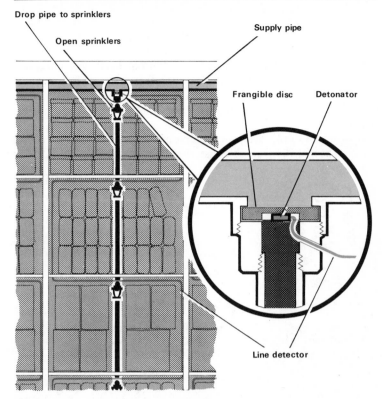

Fig. 9.1 Layout of pipework and line detector in racking, for one zone.

insulation round the twisted pair give protection against mechanical damage, moisture, etc. On heating to 68°C, the innermost layer of insulation melts and a good contact is made between the two wires. This allows a current to flow which fires a detonator causing the centre of a frangible disc to disintegrate (Fig. 9.2); the pieces are

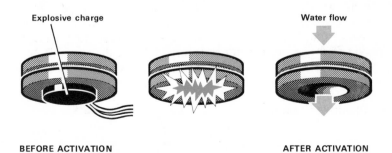

Fig. 9.2 Nylon frangible disc in housing before and after detonation.

washed away as the water is released and rushes to the open sprinklers. In experimental tests this system achieved more rapid extinction than the normal system.

Frangible discs currently in use are nylon which have been found to sag with age and dislodge or weaken the effect of the explosive charge which is simply glued to the underside. Steps are now being taken to develop a metal frangible disc with the explosive charge set into the centre of it.

A variation of this system uses a modified type of multiple control valve in lieu of the frangible disc (Fig. 9.3). An igniter cord or line

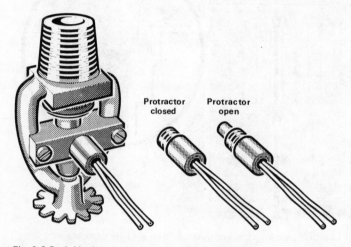

Fig. 9.3 Sprinkler head with 'actuator' (protractor type).

detector is connected to the actuator which holds a small explosive charge. When activated by the cord or detector, the explosive charge pushes out a small stud in the protractor; this breaks the sprinkler bulb and allows water to flow. Should the actuator fail for any reason, the glass bulb will operate in the normal way when the pre-determined temperature is reached. Such a system is probably too expensive to fit to individual sprinkler heads, but it can be used effectively with groups of four or more on a multiple control basis to achieve a quicker discharge of water for certain risks. While the frangible disc system operates on the vertical plane, this type of quick-acting sprinkler will work on a horizontal plane.

b. Sprinkler heads
In high-racked storage normal sprinkler heads with their yoke arms and deflector plates are particularly vulnerable when pallets are being moved in and out. The development of the high-speed sprinkler system described above has helped to provide a solution to this. As it

uses open sprinklers which do not require a thermal element or its housing, the opportunity has been taken to develop 'in-line' sprinklers (see Plate 9) which can be installed into the vertical feed pipes of the system.

A water spray from the sprinkler is produced by impinging jets of water caused by forcing the water through small holes which can be seen in the sprinklers in the photograph. In practice it has been found that this gives a symmetrical and satisfactory water distribution. This 'in-line' sprinkler has advantages over the normal type: it is robust, simple, cheap to make, has no moving parts and is unlikely to suffer damage.

c. Other developments

Recent tests have been conducted on various sprinkler configurations within high-racked storages. For example, in one test sprinklers were fitted along both faces and along the centre of the racking at one level, but along the centre only at a higher level (Fig. 9.4). Those along the centre at both levels were fitted alternately.

This configuration proved no more effective than the Fire Offices' Committee recommended layout in controlling a fire. However, it was found that if this experimental configuration was used with a thick plywood barrier inserted at the first level of sprinklers (the central sprinklers at this level were not therefore used), upward spread of fire was reduced, but this was at the expense of sideways spread.

Experiments are continuing to find a more highly efficient sprinkler system for this particular type of risk.

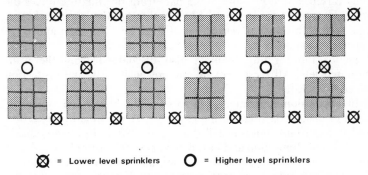

⊗ = Lower level sprinklers   ◯ = Higher level sprinklers

Fig. 9.4 Plan showing the special sprinkler layout for high-racked storage.

2 Ground level sprinklers

A new system of ground level sprinklers has recently been designed for the protection of aircraft maintenance and assembly areas. It is being used by the British Aircraft Corporation to protect the Concorde assembly area. The protection of this type of risk presents problems for the traditional sprinkler installation. The size and shape of aircraft under construction shields a large area of ground from an overhead system. The Aircraft Assembly Hall at Filton is 321 metres wide and 128 metres deep at the centre bay and 82 metres deep at each of the east and west bays. The problem has been overcome by sinking the sprinkler nozzles in the floor and causing them to rise automatically in a fire situation (see Plate 10).

The protected area is divided into zones on a square grid pattern and in the BAC system an average of 110 nozzles are installed in each zone. These nozzles are housed in cast-iron cylinders buried in the concrete floor and are covered with loosely fitting steel caps which lie flush with the floor. This allows access to the nozzles for testing and inspection purposes. Coupled with this ground sprinkler system is a series of wall-mounted overwing oscillating jets which are set to discharge at an angle range of 60 degrees over a horizontal distance of more than 50 metres.

Automatic flame detectors are used to activate the system. 'Infrascan' detectors are mounted at roof level and 'Infrastat' (i.e. static) detectors are mounted where required 3 metres above the ground to detect underwing fires. In order to avoid unnecessary operation the system will only be activated when two detectors have confirmed the flame source: this need only be a matter of 15 to 20 seconds, and then only the sprinklers in the affected zone will operate.

The extinguishing agent used is aqueous film-forming foam (AFFF) and the foam concentrate is kept in tanks outside the hangar. Once the system is activated, the foam concentrate and water are automatically mixed, and a pressure of 3.5 bars from this mixture forces the sprinkler nozzles to rise about 120 mm through the loose steel caps. The nozzles produce a vertical jet at least 5 metres high and three peripheral jets which gives a ground spray of about 8 metres diameter. Aqueous film-forming foam is also discharged from the wall-mounted jets. All these provide comprehensive external protection for each aircraft.

In conclusion it is interesting to consider briefly the system of internal protection used during assembly. A portable fire detection and extinguishing unit is installed in the aircraft, linked to an outside control unit. Ionisation and heat detectors in the portable unit detect any overheating in the instrumentation and miles of related cables. The detectors, when activated, operate a BCF container fitted in the portable unit.

A portable system of this type may have other uses, for instance in the installation stages of a computer, prior to the fixing of a permanent extinguishing system. Hotels or conference centres may also find it useful where they are mounting exhibitions of a temporary nature for which additional fire protection is insisted on by the exhibitors or insurers.

Part 2
Fire alarm systems

An alarm of fire can be raised automatically by a detection system or manually by a person in the affected building.

Many fires however are not discovered in their early stages by occupants of the premises involved but are revealed only when they have developed sufficiently to become noticeable to passers by and have caused considerable damage. Such delays in fires being discovered and further delays in calling the fire brigade are major factors contributing to heavy fire losses.

In view of this it will be appreciated that automatic detection and alarm systems offer particular advantages with their potential for quick detection and automatic alarm. This is especially so in premises which are unoccupied at night, week-ends and during holiday periods. Fire insurers are prepared to offer insurance premium rebates, in certain classes of occupancy, where efficient automatic detection and alarm systems are installed. The Fire Offices' Committee of the insurance companies issue rules which detail their requirements in this respect.

Recommended specifications and requirements in connection with the design and installation of electrical fire alarm systems are also issued by the British Standards Institution (BS 3116—4 parts and BS 5839 Pt. 1.

Chapter 10
Automatic fire detectors—general

The prime function of a fire detector is to detect one or more changes in the protected environment indicative of the development of a fire condition. Usually mounted on ceilings or in air ducts detectors are activated in the main by smoke or radiation. These conditions can be readily identified with important stages in the development of a fire:

(i)   After ignition has occurred, and the *invisible* products of combustion are being released.

(ii) When *visible* smoke is being produced.

(iii) When the fire is producing flame and a degree of illumination.

(iv) When the temperature in the vicinity of the fire rises rapidly or reaches a predetermined figure.

The types of detector designed to operate at one of these particular stages are as follows:

(i)   Ionisation detector⎫
                          ⎬ smoke detectors
(ii) Optical detector   ⎭

(iii) Radiation detector

(iv) Heat detector

The final choice of detector type has to be based on the risk to be protected and the individual circumstances of each case.

The main groups of detector system in use are those actuated by smoke and those actuated by heat.

Whatever detector is employed, however, it needs to be reliable, robust and economical.

The sequence of events in an automatic fire alarm system using automatic fire detection will usually be as shown in Fig. 10.1, although in many instances now the alarm is not transmitted direct to the fire brigade but via a commercially-operated Central station (see the *Manual of Firemanship, Book 10, 'Fire brigade communications'*).

Descriptions of some of the various detectors available and the basic circuits and equipment used are included in this Part.

The chapters on detectors examine the principles of the three main types (smoke, radiation and heat). They then go on, in each case, to

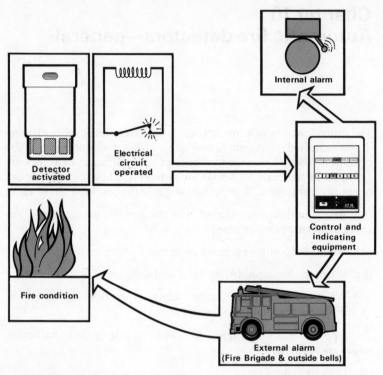

Fig. 10.1 Diagrammatic illustration of an automatic fire alarm system. (Note: In some instances the automatic detector will also operate a fire extinguishing system as described in Part 1.)

describe how these principles are applied to some current models. The models used are necessarily only a representative selection of the wide range available.

There is a glossary on page 179 of terms used in conjunction with automatic fire detection and alarm systems and with which you may be unfamiliar.

Not all the symbols used in the diagrams comply with those recommended in the British Standard 1635—Graphical symbols and abbreviations for fire protection drawings.

Chapter 11
Smoke detectors

1 Ionisation detector

It was realised as early as 1922 that an ionisation chamber could be used for detecting impurities in the air but the development had little application outside the laboratory until the 1940's. Since 1945 the technique has been developed still further into a complete system for signalling the presence of *invisible* products of combustion—normally long before any flame, or even a large amount of smoke or heat, is generated.

a. The theory

What is 'ionisation'? An atom is made up of protons, electrons and neutrons, the protons and electrons being in balance as shown below (three of each in this case).

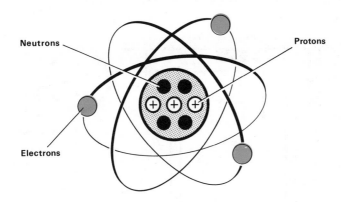

Fig. 11.1 Diagram of an atom.

If the atom is subjected to radiation from a radioactive source some electrons are knocked off. As a result the atom becomes positively charged (i.e. it has more protons than electrons); the 'free' electron quickly links up with another atom which becomes negatively charged (i.e. more electrons than protons). These 'new' atoms are called 'ions' and the process that creates them 'ionisation' (Fig. 11.2).
If the atoms of air in a container are subjected to radiation,

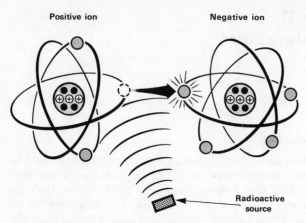

Fig. 11.2 Illustration of ionisation.

ionisation takes place in the same way, but the ions will be moving about haphazardly. If we then introduce a positively-charged plate and a negatively-charged plate to the container a more orderly and predictable movement of ions takes place; the positive ions are attracted to the negative plate and the negative ions are attracted to the positive plate.

This forms the basis of the ionisation dectector (Fig. 11.3).

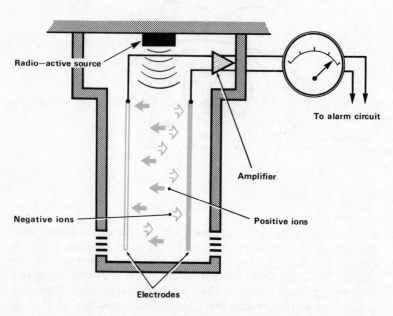

Fig. 11.3 Diagram of an ionisation detector (non-fire condition).

92

The movement of ions between the plates in the chamber reduces the resistance of the air so that a small electric current flows in the external circuit. The current is small and is amplified so that it can be readily monitored.

In a fire condition (Fig. 11.4) smoke particles entering the chamber become attached to the ions because of electrostatic attraction and slow their movement. This causes a reduction in the current flow. When the current falls below a predetermined level the amplifier senses it and initiates an alarm. That is the basic concept of the ionisation detector—in practice it is a little more sophisticated as can be seen from the following paragraphs.

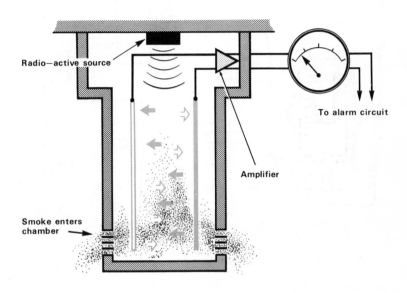

Fig. 11.4 Diagram of an ionisation detector (fire condition).

b. The practice

An illustration of one type of a double chamber ionisation detector is shown in Fig. 11.5 (see also Plate 11). One ionisation chamber is in a semi-sealed environment which does not permit the entry of smoke, the other is open to the atmosphere and therefore permits smoke to enter.

In normal conditions both the inner and open chambers will be free from smoke and form a balanced electrical circuit. In a 'non-fire' condition the voltage at (1) is insufficient to fire the cold cathode tube (2) which acts as a switch controlling the operation of the relay.

When smoke enters the open chamber, however, it will slow the move-ment of ions as described earlier. As the movement of ions is slowed only in the open chamber this effectively unbalances the electrical circuit—in simple terms the open chamber now offers a higher resistance to the flow of electricity than the inner chamber does. This increases the voltage at (1) and causes the cold cathode tube to 'strike' thus forming a high current path to operate the relay and hence sound the alarm.

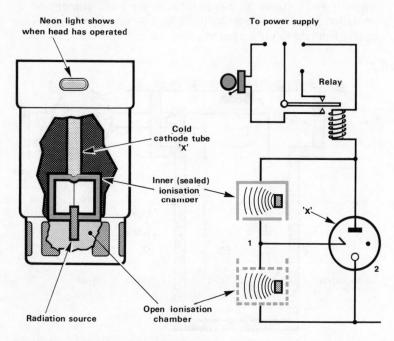

Fig. 11.5 Illustration of an ionisation detector.

Although this example, for ease of illustration, shows a cold cathode tube as the amplifier and 'switch mechanism', solid state amplifiers (using transistors etc.) are used to perform this function in some ionisation detectors.

An advantage of the ionisation detector is its sensitivity in the early stages of a fire when smoke particles are small. Because of this sensitivivy care must be taken in the siting of detector heads. In some locations such as a garage or kitchen the products of combustion could be present in 'non-fire' conditions. Siting ionisation detectors in these areas could result in repeated false alarms.

It is particularly important that the detectors are not placed near a ventilator or fresh air inlet where a current of clean air can pass over them and inhibit their speed of reaction in a fire situation.

Most types of ionisation detector head are designed to be mounted on the ceiling and usually provide adequate coverage for 100 square metres of floor area. With slight modifications they can be fitted in air ducts for air-cooled machinery and thus give early warning of possible fire damage to intricate and expensive equipment.

Ionisation detectors with single chambers have been produced using a capacitor as a replacement for the second (inner) chamber. They have not been widely used however and the two-chamber type described above is the one most commonly found.

2 Optical detector

While the ionisation detector responds to the invisible products of combustion the optical detector, as its name implies, reacts to the *visible* products of combustion, i.e. the particles of carbon and other chemicals which give smoke its characteristic appearance. An optical detector has two important components, a light source and a photo-electric cell. It is the amount of light falling on the photo-electric cell, which is the critical factor in the operation of the optical detector. Some optical detectors are designed so that, in a fire situation, MORE light is thrown onto the photo-electric cell. These are called the 'light-scatter type'.

Others are designed so that LESS light is thrown onto the photo-electric cell in a fire situation. These are called the 'obscuration type'.

a. The light-scatter type

(1) The theory

The light source and photo-electric cell are mounted in a light-proof housing which is designed to allow smoke to flow into it unimpeded. In the 'non-fire' condition light from the light source does not fall on to the photo-electric cell. Fig. 11.6 shows a light-scatter type in this condition.

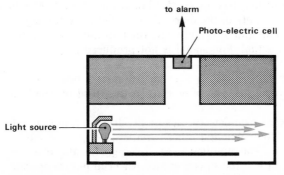

Fig. 11.6 An optical smoke detector 'light-scatter type' (non-fire) condition.

When smoke particles enter the housing, however, some light is deflected upward onto the photo-electric cell. In response to the light falling onto it the cell will either create an electrical current in the detector circuit or allow more current to flow through it (depending on the type of cell being used). The small increase in current is normally amplified by a transistorised circuit in order to energise a relay which controls the alarm. The detector is preset so that the alarm is given when the smoke density reaches a predetermined level (Fig. 11.7).

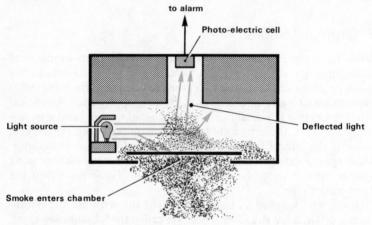

Fig. 11.7 An optical smoke detector 'light-scatter type' (fire condition).

(2) The practice

The 'light-scatter type' of optical detector is the more common of the two types previously mentioned. See Fig. 11.8 and Plate 12.

Smoke entering the detector through the smoke chamber scatters light onto the photo-electric cell. The small electrical charge produced by this is amplified and actuates an alarm relay. This raises the alarm and also switches on the indicator lamp on the detector, thus identifying the head that has operated. Should there be a failure in the power or light supply in the detector, a special relay will signal this at a central point and also illuminate the indicator lamp on the detector head; an actual 'fire' signal is not produced in these conditions.

This particular smoke detector also incorporates a heat detector using a bimetal strip (this type of detector is described in detail on page 112).

The area protected by a detector head will vary depending on the risk involved, the floor plan and other variables, but general guidelines can be given. The nominal area coverage for the detector illustrated in Fig. 11.8 is 100 square metres per head but for specific risks or areas this figure can decrease or increase.

As with the ionisation detector it is possible, with modifications, to mount some optical detectors in air ducts etc. for the protection of cabling and machinery.

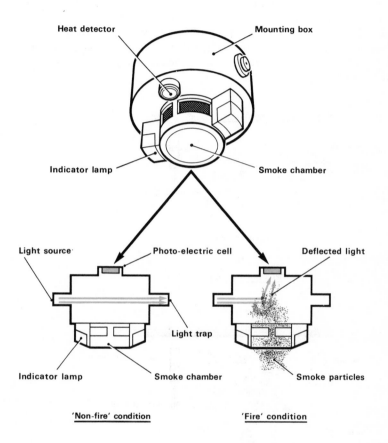

Fig. 11.8 Honeywell (Pyrotector) optical smoke detector.

b. Obscuration type

(1) The theory

The obscuration type optical detector works on the reverse of the principle just described—the light is obscured by the smoke. The resultant reduction in the intensity of light falling on the photo-electric cell causes an alarm signal to be raised. This principle is illustrated in Fig. 11.9.

97

(2) The practice

This type of optical detector can be particularly useful for the protection of large areas. It is possible with only one detector to throw the light beam anything from 3 metres to 45 metres with a sensitivity of about 6 metres on either side. The light source and lens will be housed at one end of the protected area with the photo-electric cell at the opposite end (this is similar to the arrangement for the infra-red beam fire detection system described on page 101). The principle can also be used in individual detector heads on a similar basis to the light-scatter type.

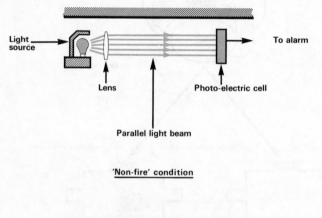

'Non-fire' condition

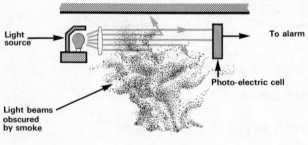

'Fire' condition

Fig. 11.9 Optical detector—'obscuration type'.

Light emitting diodes (L.E.D's) are now widely used as the light source in optical detectors instead of tungsten filament lamps. They consume very little current and provide a more efficient and longer lasting source of light.

c. Sampling detector

Brief mention needs to be made of sampling detectors. They comprise a series of small bore sampling tubes which are located in the fire risk zone. These sampling tubes are connected to a central monitor unit. The monitor unit continuously samples the atmosphere in the protected zone by drawing air through small holes in the tubes by means of a motor-driven fan. This air is then passed through an ionisation chamber similar in most respects to that described at the beginning of this chapter. The ionisation chamber is designed to raise the alarm when the level of combustion products reaches a predetermined level.

Conclusion

The detection of fire by smoke detectors is dependent on a number of factors, e.g. smoke concentration, size and shape of smoke particles. The wide variety of smoke produced by different materials complicates the situation. Generally in the early stages of most fires the smoke particles are small, but as the fire ages they tend to conglomerate to form larger particles.

The ionisation detector actually detects smoke particles and is therefore dependent on the fire producing them; as a general rule it is more sensitive to the smaller, normally invisible, smoke particles. This makes it particularly useful in the early stages of relatively clean burning fires (e.g. of wood and paper). It will not, however, always operate in the presence of 'cold' smoke. The optical detector is more efficient in situations where the protected risk is likely to give rise to dense smoke (i.e. larger particles) in the earlier stages of a fire as in some burning plastics.

In the main earlier detection can be obtained with a smoke sensitive system than with a heat sensitive one.

Chapter 12
Radiation detectors

As well as producing hot 'gases' fire releases radiant energy (Fig. 12.1) in the form of:

(i)   Infra-red radiation

(ii) Visible light

(iii) Ultra-violet radiation.

These forms of energy travel in waves radiating from their point of origin and radiation detectors are designed to respond to this radiation.

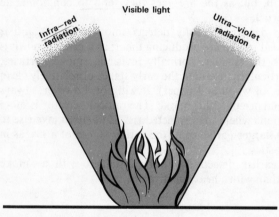

Fig. 12.1 Illustration of forms of radiant energy produced by a fire.

Obviously the use of the visible light band to activate a detector would present many problems because the detector would not be able to differentiate between the various legitimate sources of visible light and those created by a fire. In practice therefore these detectors are designed to respond specifically to either:

(1)   Infra-red radiation
       or
(2)   ultra violet radiation

using a photo-electric cell which is sensitive to one of these sources.

1 Infra-red detector

a. The theory

The basic components of the infra-red detector are shown in Fig. 12.2.

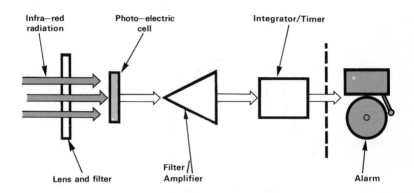

Fig. 12.2 Schematic diagram of components of an infra-red detector.

It is obviously necessary to protect the photo-electric cell and electrical components from dirt and moisture but the protective covering must allow the infra-red radiation to pass through it. Not all material is transparent to infra-red but quartz is and is commonly used as the protective shield in these detectors. The lens and filter will allow only infra-red radiation to fall on to the photo-electric cell. On being struck by the radiation, the cell will transmit a signal to the filter/amplifier. Flame, however, may not be the only producer of infra-red radiation in the protected area; there may be a limited number of other producers e.g. sunlight or heaters, but flame has a distinctive flicker, normally in the frequency range of 4 Hz–15 Hz. The function of the filter/amplifier, therefore, is not only to amplify but also to filter out signals not in this range. If the signal is in this range (4 Hz–15 Hz) it is then fed to the integrator/timer which will activate the alarm circuit only if the signal persists for a pre-set period (normally 2–15 secs). While this small delay may slightly off-set the quick response time of the detector, it is necessary if false alarms are to be kept to a minimum. Once any signal is rejected the detector goes back on standby.

b. The practice

Fig. 12.3 shows how these components are fitted into an actual detector (see also Plate 13). This detector has a neon flasher to indicate which head has been activated.

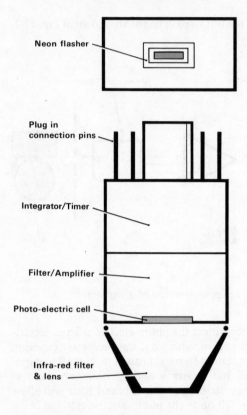

Neon flasher

Plug in
connection pins

Integrator/Timer

Filter/Amplifier

Photo-electric cell

Infra-red filter
& lens

Fig. 12.3 Schematic diagram of an infra-red radiation detector.

As an infra-red detector must 'see' a flame before it will raise an alarm the one illustrated in Fig. 12.3 is useful where the risk is divided into compartments or is a congested area in which visibility might be impaired. Individual detector heads can protect each compartment or be placed in strategic positions in the congested area.

For larger areas, free of congestion and with a more open plan a scanning infra-red detector is available. One of these is illustrated in Plate 14 and Fig. 12.4.

The deflector continually scans the protected area (approximately every 20 seconds). This enables the detector to monitor 360 degrees in the horizontal plane and a wide angle on the vertical plane. Immediately the photo-electric cell is struck by deflected infra-red radiation and the characteristic 'flicker' is identified by the filter/amplifier, the integrator stops the motor in order that the deflector can 'view' the flame source directly and allow the radiation to fall continuously on the photo-electric cell.

The timer can then check whether the flame flicker persists for the 2–15 seconds as explained earlier. Where the infra-red source is present beyond this period the alarm is raised; if it is not present the integrator restarts the deflector motor putting the detector back on standby.

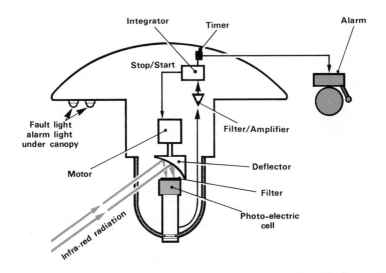

Fig. 12.4 Diagram of an infra-scan radiation detector.

The infra-scan detector has an amber fault light which will light up a few seconds after a fault is detected; the red alarm light illuminates once the integrator activates the alarm.

The domed cover is thermally insulated and the cell and deflector are shielded by a quartz globe.

Theoretically there is no limit to the range of the infra-scan detector but for quick detection in the early stages of a fire the radius of detection should be limited to about 90 metres.

A much greater area of coverage can be obtained from the scanning type than from the static type but which type is used in any particular situation will depend on the interior plan and use of the protected area. Infra-red detectors can provide rapid detection in risk areas where flame is likely to develop at an early stage of combustion. This is because of the almost instantaneous transmission of radiation.

Unlike smoke or heat detectors which can only be used indoors, the infra-red detector can be equally efficient inside or out. This is because it simply needs to 'see' the flame, whereas smoke or heat

detectors have to rely on ceilings or walls to direct combustion products to the sensing head.

This latter factor makes the infra-red detector (especially the
scanning type) useful for protection of open storage areas (e.g.
timber yards and fuel depots). When used in these situations, false
alarms have been caused by sunlight reflected from car windows,
rippling pools etc. These occurrences, however, are rare and do not
seriously detract from the detector's suitability.

2 Ultra-violet detector

a. The theory

Like the infra-red detector, this detector also needs to be able to 'see'
the flame before it will operate, but since legitimate sources of ultra-
violet radiation are very limited, flicker discrimination is not needed.

Basically the ultra-violet detector consists of an amplifier and a
photo-electric cell or gas-filled tube sensitive to ultra-violet radiation
(Fig. 12.5).

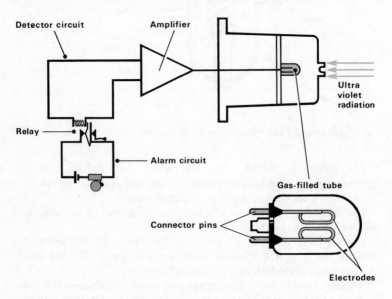

Fig. 12.5 Diagrammatic illustration of an ultra-violet detector.

b. The practice

The principle of operation is very similar to that of the ionisation
detector. When ultra-violet radiation strikes the gas filled tube it
ionises the gas in the tube. A small current is set up between the two
electrodes and the tube becomes a conductor of electricity. When the

current flow is greater than the set point of the amplifier the alarm relay closes immediately and causes the alarm to sound. The circuit can also have an integrator incorporated in it which will effectively delay the alarm for 10–15 seconds. This can reduce false alarms from legitimate external sources of ultra-violet radiation like lightning.

The detector is not affected by sunlight or artificial light but is sensitive to electrical arcs and would not therefore be recommended for areas in which welding was being done.

In practice the ultra-violet detector is most commonly used for specialised applications such as the monitoring of aircraft engine nacelles, but it can be used to protect fuel storage tanks, oil drilling rigs, warehouses, paint spray booths etc.

An example of an ultra-violet detector head and an amplifier is shown in Plate 15. In this case the amplifier will cater for as many as four detector heads which can be mounted up to 300 metres from it. The detector has a 90-degree angle of vision and will detect 1.8 square metres of flame at a distance of 12 metres.

Conclusion

Radiation detectors have a quick response capability and as they are not dependent on combustion products actually reaching the detector head, they can be used out of doors. They do, however, need a clear 'view' of the protected area and any lenses or covers must be kept clean if efficiency is not to be impaired. Early warning will obviously only be achieved if the goods or materials being protected are readily flammable. The relative amount of smoke likely to be produced by the goods is another important factor. In a smoky fire infra-red detectors may be preferable to ultra-violet types because infra-red radiation can penetrate smoke better, but where goods are likely to smoulder and produce smoke for a long period before flames appear, radiation detectors are obviously of little value.

Chapter 13
Heat detectors

Heat detectors are designed to detect fire in its more advanced stages when the temperature in the protected area starts to rise. Given that the effects of heat are easy to observe it is not surprising that heat detectors were the earliest form of detector to be developed.

The effects of heat which provide the basic operating principles for heat detectors are:

(1) Melting (or fusion) in metals

(2) Expansion in solids, gases and liquids

(3) The electrical effect.

These explain to some extent, why there is such a wide choice in methods of heat detection.

This chapter explains, in turn, each one of the above effects and detectors which use them.

In discussing heat detectors reference will be made to 'fixed temperature' detectors and 'rate-of-rise' detectors. A 'fixed temperature' detector is one that responds only when a predetermined temperature is reached.

A 'rate-of-rise' detector is one that responds when the temperature rise is abnormally rapid.

In practice 'rate-of-rise' detectors generally incorporate a fixed temperature device in accordance with British Standard 3116 for heat detectors. This is particularly useful where a very slow growing fire would not generate heat sufficiently rapidly to operate the 'rate-of-rise' element.

1 Heat detectors using fusible alloys

a. The theory

These detectors are based on the fact that certain metals—alloys are normally used—melt at relatively low temperatures; the general range available extends from about 55°C to 180°C. As the metal used predetermines the temperature at which the alarm will sound it will be chosen after due consideration of the type of risk to be protected and the normal ambient temperature in the protected area.

b. The practice

(i) *The 'Dimac' detector:*

This detector (Fig. 13.1) consists of a fixed contact blade (1) and a pair of spring contacts (2) and (3) held under tension by a fusible alloy link. In this condition the electric circuit is incomplete and the alarm is not activated. When the surrounding air reaches the predetermined melting point of the fusible link (a range of 49°C to 144°C is available in this case) the spring contacts separate and (2) makes contact with (1). This completes the circuit and sounds the alarm.

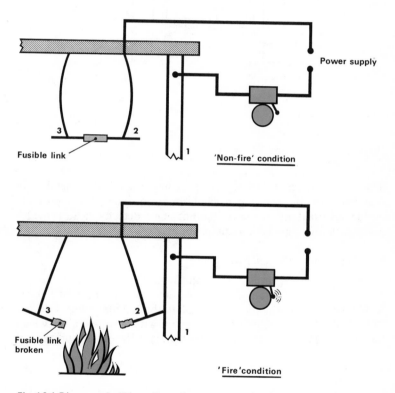

Fig. 13.1 Diagram of a 'Dimac' heat detector.

It is also possible to use spring contacts (2) and (3) as the electrical contacts. In this case a relay has to be incorporated into the system to 'hold off' the alarm. When the fusible link melts the circuit is broken, the relay de-energised and the alarm sounds.

An illustration of the detector's mechanism is shown in Fig. 13.2.

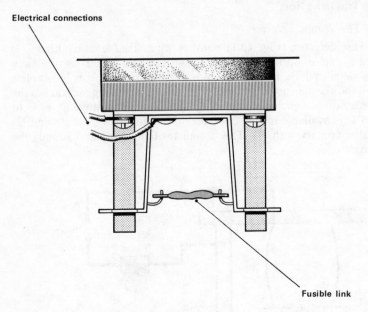

Electrical connections

Fusible link

Fig. 13.2 Mechanism of a 'Dimac' heat detector.

The 'Dimac' detector is designed for ceiling mounting. A metal grille (see Plate 16) protects the mechanism from damage and prevents accidental breaking of the fusible link. One detector head provides protection for an area of 50 square metres.

(ii) *Break-link cable heat detector:*

As can be seen from Fig. 13.3 (and Plate 17) this is quite a simple device and a good example of a line detector. A length of flexible PVC insulated, conductor cable is cut at about 2 metre intervals and the bared ends are joined together again with a fusible alloy which has a low melting point. The cable is held taut by tension springs and

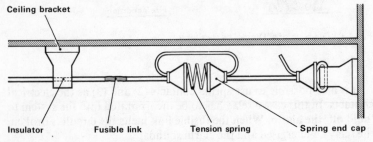

Ceiling bracket

Insulator   Fusible link   Tension spring   Spring end cap

Fig. 13.3 Diagram of a break-link cable heat detector.

the whole assembly is mounted parallel to the ceiling on moulded insulators (normally spaced about 7.5 metres apart).

In a 'non-fire' condition current flows continuously through the cable. Once the predetermined temperature is reached however (a range of 49°C to 88°C is available in this case) the alloy link melts and breaks the circuit thus raising the alarm. Each link will protect an area of 50 square metres.

(iii) *Pyrene 30 D detector:*

This detector (Fig. 13.4 and Plate 18) comprises a thin walled metal case fitted with heat collecting fins at its lower end. A conductor extends through the core and the metal casing is lined with fusible alloy which acts as a second conductor. Heat from a fire will melt the fusible alloy at the predetermined temperature and cause it to make contact with the central conductor. This completes an electrical circuit to sound the alarm.

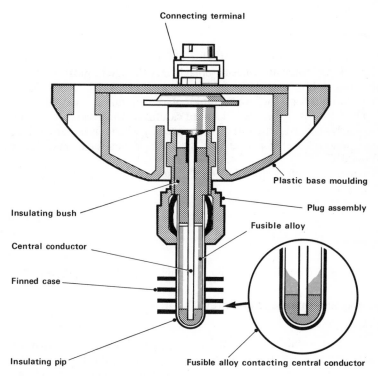

Fig. 13.4 'Pyrene 30D' heat detector.

The range of operating temperatures for this detector is 57°C to 102°C, and each detector head will protect about 36 square metres.

(iv) *Thermostatic cable:*

Thermostatic cable is a co-axial type cable in which one conductor is totally enclosed by the other conductor. The polythene insulating medium in which the inner core is embedded melts at a comparatively low temperature (approx. 96°C) so that in a fire condition both conductors make contact and sound the alarm.

While thermostatic cable is not recommended as a detector in its own right some manufacturers recommend that as an additional safeguard it can be used for heat detector circuits. Effective protection can thus be given to ducts, underfloor cavities, lofts and similar locations where it might be impracticable to install a standard detector unit. This is one of the few contexts in which fusible plastic can be used as the operating element in a detection system. It also has uses in conjunction with some fixed installations where the melting of nylon tubing or a nylon line will cause the release of an extinguishing medium (usually dry powder) on to the affected area.

General

Fusible link detectors are not self-righting. Once they have operated the link or fusible alloy needs replacing. Although in most cases this is a reasonably straightforward operation, it needs to be remembered that the detector is ineffective until replacement takes place.

Detectors using fusible links need careful treatment and should be regularly checked—the soft metal, especially when it is under tension, may weaken over a period and the springs themselves may suffer fatigue.

All the detectors described in this section are fixed temperature detectors.

2 Heat detectors using the principle of expansion

a. Expansion of a single metal strip

(1) The theory

A piece of metal will expand when heated; this expansion is most noticeable in a length of metal with its ends unrestrained.

If both ends of the metal are secured to a solid base and the metal is then subjected to heat the effect of the expansion is to cause the metal strip to bow (Fig.13.5). If contacts are added as shown in the diagram the principle can be used in a detector to complete an electrical circuit when a predetermined temperature is reached.

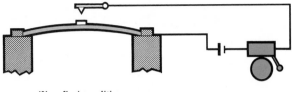

'Non-fire' condition

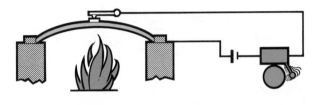

Fire condition

Fig. 13.5 Illustration of the expansion of the metal strip with secured ends.

(2) The practice

(i) *'Fidela' heat detector:*

The heat sensitive element in the 'Fidela' detector (Fig. 13.6) is a thin stainless steel strip, which is pre-stressed and secured by tensioning studs to a steel base.

A contact pin is pivoted at the centre of the strip. When subjected to heat the metal strip bows and causes the pin to close the contact points and operate the alarm. The nominal operating temperature for this detector is 65°C and the maximum area protected by one head is 50 square metres (see Plate 19).

(ii) *The 'May-Oatway' heat detector:*

The 'May-Oatway' is a line detector using a single copper wire as the sensing element. The copper wire is fixed to a steel channel 2.2 metres long which is fitted parallel to the ceiling. Suspended from the length of copper wire is a small PVC sac which holds a gas-filled tube containing two electric contacts and a globule of mercury.

When the copper wire is subjected to heat the resultant expansion causes it to sag (Fig. 13.7) tilting the PVC sac and causing the mercury to cover the electrical contacts. This completes the circuit and raises the alarm.

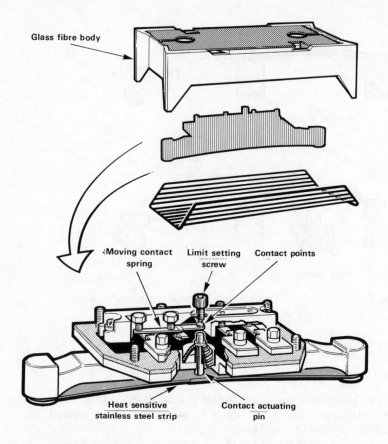

Glass fibre body

Moving contact spring

Limit setting screw

Contact points

Heat sensitive stainless steel strip

Contact actuating pin

Fig. 13.6 Exploded diagram of a 'Fidela' heat detector.

The maximum area covered by the detector is (approx.) 70 square metres (see Plate 20).

(Mercury switches, as used in this detector, are useful in preventing faulty contacts in damp or abnormally dirty locations).

The detector described above is the 'May-Oatway' Mk 1. There is a Mk 2 version available for installation in highly corrosive atmospheres. Its operation is the same as in the Mk 1 but treated stainless steel fittings are used and a pointer and calibrated scale provided to facilitate initial setting up.

b. Expansion of a bimetal strip

(1) The theory

The bimetal strip is a development of the basic principle of the expan-

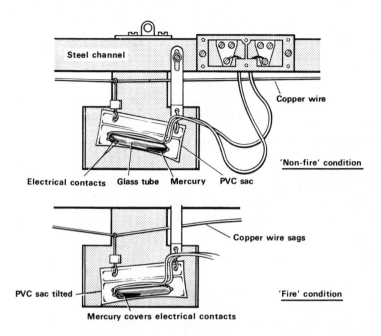

Fig. 13.7 Detail of a 'May-Oatway' heat detector.

sion of metals due to heat. It is widely used in heat detectors and also as the thermostat in household goods, such as electric kettles and irons. The bimetal strip makes use of the fact that when heated some metals expand at a greater rate than others (Fig. 13.8).

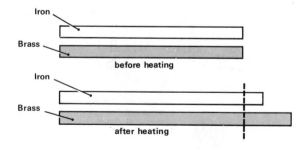

Fig. 13.8 Illustration of differing rates of metal expansion.

If these two metals are bonded together to form a bimetal strip and then subjected to heat the strip will bend (Fig. 13.9) to accommodate

E

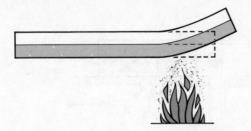

Fig. 13.9 Illustration of the effect of heat on a bimetal strip.

the differing rates of expansion. The strip will always bend towards the metal with the lower rate of expansion. Fig. 13.10 shows the use of a bimetal strip as a heat detector.

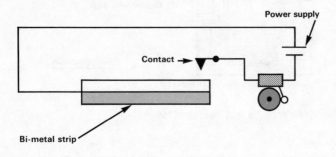

'Non-fire' condition

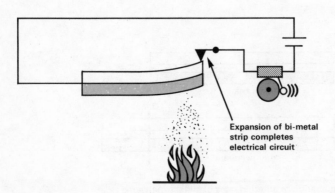

Expansion of bi-metal strip completes electrical circuit

'Fire' condition

Fig. 13.10 Illustration of a bimetal strip as a heat detector.

The advantage of a bimetal strip over a single metal strip is the greater movement resulting from a given rise in temperature.

(2) The practice

The 'Gents 1151' detector uses a bimetal strip as the heat sensing element (Plate 21).

The strip is held in place by a pivot at one end and rests on a latch at the other end (Fig. 13.11(1)). A mercury switch (similar to that used in the 'May-Oatway' detector) is secured to the housing holding the bimetal strip.

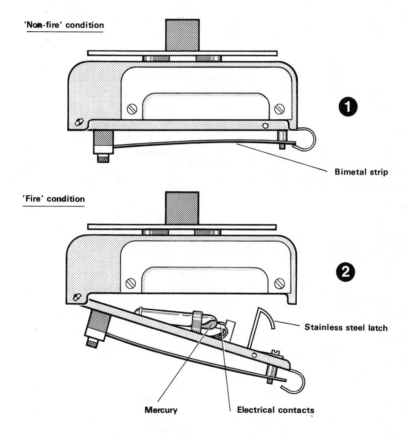

Fig. 13.11 'Gents 1151' heat detector (1) non-fire condition (2) fire condition.

With a rise in temperature the bimetal strip bows and at the pre-determined temperature (normally 65°C) frees itself from the latch (Fig. 13.11(2)) and tilts the mercury tube; the mercury covers the electrical contacts completing the circuit, causing the alarm to sound.

This tilting of the bottom portion of the detector allows quick identification of the head that has operated.

Each detector can protect an area of 36 square metres.

c. Expansion of bimetal strips in a 'rate-of-rise' detector

(1) The theory

Bimetal strips are also used as the heat sensitive elements in some 'rate-of-rise' detectors. Their principle of operation is explained below.

Two similar composition bimetal strips are used but one is suitably shielded and protected to reduce its rate of expansion (Fig. 13.12(1)).

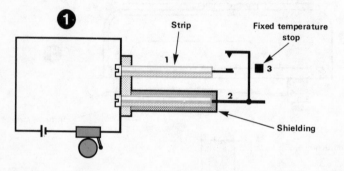

Fig. 13.12 (1) Illustration of 'rate-of-rise' principle—'non-fire' condition.

If there is a rapid rise in temperature (Fig.13.12(2)) strip (1), which is not shielded, will expand more rapidly than strip (2) and as a result will quickly make contact with it.

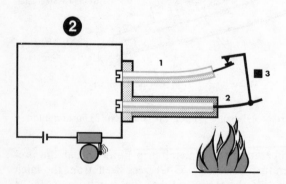

Fig. 13.12 (2) Illustration of 'rate-of-rise' principle—rapid rise in temperature.

Where there is a slow rise in temperature (Fig. 13.12(3)) the slow rate of expansion in both strips keeps them, relatively, the same distance apart. In other words the movement of strip (2) compensates for the gradual rise in ambient temperature which might be quite normal in certain locations. It is undesirable however for this situation to continue too long when a slow burning fire might be the cause of the

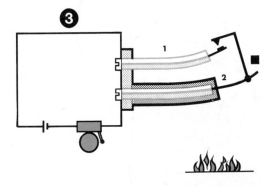

Fig. 13.12 (3) Illustration of 'rate-of-rise' principle—slow rise in temperature.

temperature rise. For this reason (as mentioned at the beginning of this Chapter) a fixed temperature device (3) is fitted in 'rate-of-rise' detectors. This will stop the movement of strip (2) when a predetermined temperature is reached and thus allow strip (1) to catch up and make the necessary contact to raise an alarm.

(2) The practice

In this detector (Fig. 13.13 and Plate 22) two bimetal strips are curved to fit inside the cylindrical container, the top half of which is thick plastic and the bottom half aluminium. The plastic base moulding effectively shields the upper strip while the lower strip is subjected to greater heat through the thin aluminium cover.

With a rapid rise in temperature the strips expand within the circumference of the container. Because of its greater rate of expansion the lower strip quickly makes contact with the upper strip and the alarm is raised.

In a slow burning fire situation the fixed temperature stop will eventually halt the expansion of the upper strip and thus allow the lower strip to catch up and make contact with it to raise the alarm. The fixed temperature stop can be designed to operate at 57°C or 100°C depending on the requirements of the user.

The area protected by this detector is 50 square metres.

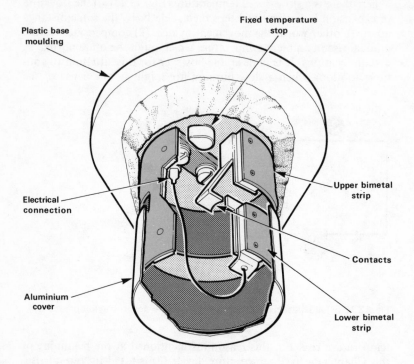

Fig. 13.13 'Pyrene' rate-of-rise heat detector.

General

The main advantage of detectors operating on the expansion-of-metal principle is that they suffer no damage from operation and are self-resetting. They are therefore back on standby automatically immediately any fire situation has been dealt with. This does not, of course, apply to detectors operating on the 'Gents 1151' principle—in these cases the metal strip will have to be pushed into place.

In the situation in which there is likely to be a large variation in ambient temperature (e.g. during normal working processes), the 'rate-of-rise' detector offers flexibility. If the normal temperature changes are gradual it will compensate for them, any rapid rise (being out of pattern anyway) will cause the alarm to be raised.

However, where a rapid rise in temperature is a normal result of the work processes being carried out, the fixed temperature detector is to be preferred. In this type of situation it is less prone to false alarms than the 'rate-of-rise' type.

A fixed temperature detector will take longer to respond in a cold area than in a warm one. This is because of the relatively longer time needed for the ambient temperature to reach the operating temperature of the detector. A 'rate-of-rise' type on the other hand will take the same time to respond in both situations—it reacts to the relative rise in temperature.

d. Expansion of gases

(1) The theory

Where gas is used as the expanding element in a heat detector, air is the gas most commonly used; such detectors are sometimes referred to as pneumatic detectors.

The basic operating principle of this type of detector is illustrated in Fig. 13.14.

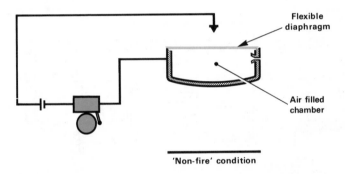

'Non-fire' condition

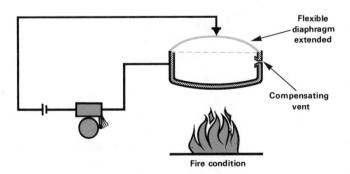

Fig. 13.14 Illustration of the principle of a pneumatic detector.

When subjected to heat the air in the chamber expands and applies pressure to the flexible diaphragm. This gradually pushes it up until it

119

meets the electrical contact, completes the circuit and raises the alarm.

By introducing a small compensating vent into the side of the air chamber (Fig. 13.14) a rate-of-rise element is added to the detector. The compensating vent will allow a certain amount of expanding air to escape; it will be carefully calibrated so as to compensate only for expansion caused by the normal and legitimate increases in the ambient temperature.

(2) The practice

(i) 'Fyrindex' automatic heat detector:

This point detector (Fig. 13.15 and Plate 23) operates on the principle of expansion of air.

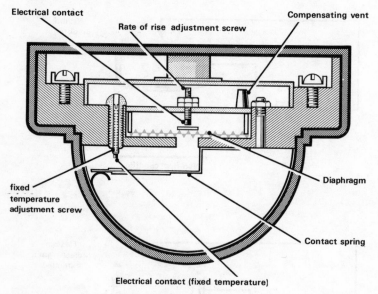

Fig. 13.15 'Fyrindex' automatic heat detector.

Fig. 13.15 shows that this is both a 'rate-of-rise' and 'fixed temperature' detector.

When there is a rapid rise in temperature the air in the chamber expands much more rapidly than the compensating vent can release it and as a result the expanding air pushes the diaphragm against the electrical contact on the base of the 'rate-of-rise' adjustment screw. This completes the circuit and raises the alarm.

If a fire develops too slowly for the 'rate-of-rise' element to detect it the 'fixed temperature' element will operate at a predetermined temperature of either 57°C or 82°C.

This is operated simply by expansion of the contact spring support which absorbs heat from the domed cover. The expanding support pushes the contact spring against the contact on the base of the fixed temperature adjustment screw thus raising the alarm. The detector resets itself after the alarm has been raised and the fire situation dealt with.

The detector is also produced as a 'rate-of-rise' type only or as a 'fixed temperature' type only.

The area protected by each head is 50 square metres.

(ii) *The 'Kidde' pneumatic 'rate-of-rise' heat detecting system:*

This system uses a hollow copper chamber as the detector head (Plate 24). It is filled with air at normal atmospheric pressure. These heads are sometimes referred to as Heat Actuated Devices (or H.A.D's). Normally fixed to the ceiling each head is connected by small bore copper tubing to a control head which houses a flexible diaphragm, a release lever and a compensating vent (Fig. 13.16).

When a detector head is subjected to heat the increased air pressure

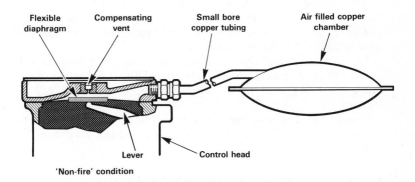

'Non-fire' condition

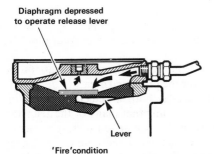

'Fire' condition

Fig. 13.16 Diagrammatic illustration of a 'Kidde' pneumatic heat detecting system.

due to expansion is transmitted through the copper tubing to the control head.

If the expansion is due to normal fluctuations in the ambient temperature the pressure is released through the compensating vent and the diaphragm and release lever remain unaffected.

Where the increase in pressure is above that allowed for by the compensating vent the diaphragm will be depressed and in turn will push down the release lever (Fig. 13.16). This completes an electrical circuit and activates the alarm.

A particular advantage of this system is that heat-actuated devices will act cumulatively—should two or more 'devices' in one group be affected by the heated air the total pressure of the expanded air in all such 'devices' becomes effective to operate the release mechanism.

These detector heads have, of course, no moving parts to go wrong.

Although this is a 'rate-of-rise' system it is possible to create a 'fixed temperature' version. To achieve this the detector is fitted with a slug of metal which seals the head from the diaphragm until the slug of metal melts at a predetermined temperature (a range from 57°C upwards is available). The metal slug will of course need replacing each time the detector head operates.

This arrangement is particularly useful where the 'devices' connected to one control head cover a variety or risks—each 'device' can be left as 'rate-of-rise' or made 'fixed temperature' depending on each specific risk being protected.

Usually six 'rate-of-rise' heat actuated devices are fitted to one control head. Where, however, 'rate-of-rise' and 'fixed temperature' types are being used in the same system, this number can be increased.

The area protected by one heat actuated device will be affected by the plan and the use being made of the area. It can vary from 27–72 square metres.

e. Expansion of liquids—the theory and practice

(1) Sprinkler systems

The liquid filled quartzoid bulbs used in sprinkler systems are probably the most common form of heat detector operating on the expansion of liquid principle.

When heated, the liquid in the bulb expands until it shatters the glass and allows water to spray over the protected area.

A sprinkler system, of course, acts as both a detection and extinguishing system and it is worth mentioning that many of the detection systems discussed in this Part are in practice linked with sprinkler or other extinguishing systems. Once activated the detector not only raises the alarm but also causes the 'sprinkler' system to release extinguishing agent into the affected area. In many cases this arrangement can reduce 'sprinkler' response time.

Sprinkler and other extinguishing systems are described in detail in Part 1 and Chapter 9, in particular, cites some examples of detectors being used to activate such installations.

(2) National tubular detector

This is the only other detector using liquid as the heat sensing element. It is no longer installed but may still be found in older buildings. A brief description only is given below.

The system consists of fluid-filled copper tubing fixed throughout the protected area. Diaphragms are fitted to both ends of the tubing and when heated, the expanding liquid extends the diaphragms. Each diaphragm carries a metal contact strip which meet when the diaphragm is extended thus completing the circuit and raising the alarm.

3 Heat detectors using the electrical effect of heat

In the past detectors have been available using either:

(i) The effect of heat on electrical resistance

or

(ii) The thermo-electric effect of heat (in a thermo-couple).

Such detectors are not now widely used, although a recently developed line detector, using a special cable as the sensing element, is now available and warrants description. Its construction is shown in Fig. 13.17.

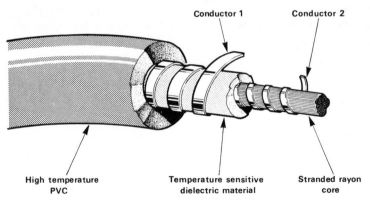

Fig. 13.17 Section of 'Alarmline' detector cable.

As can be seen from the above diagram both conductors in the cable are separated by a temperature sensitive dielectric material. When this material is subjected to heat its resistance decreases and a measurable leakage current develops.

Solid state components in the system control unit react to this change and will activate the alarm when the current reaches a pre-determined level. There are also facilities for continuously monitoring the state of the system.

The cable is (approx.) 3 mm diameter and is installed in 100-metre lengths. The manufacturer claims that it can be subjected to a temperature as high as 175°C for 25 hours and still remain intact and operative. In the majority of situations therefore, 'Alarmline' will have exactly the same potential for raising an alarm immediately after a fire as it had before the fire. This gives it an advantage over thermostatic cable which 'fuses' in a fire situation and needs replacing before it can be operative again.

Like thermostatic cable 'Alarmline' can be installed in areas with limited access (e.g. cable ducts) or areas in which it may not be practical to install traditional detectors.

General comment on heat detectors

Heat detectors, and the 'fixed temperature' type in particular, are dependent for their operation on heat being transferred from the surrounding air to the detector itself. As the air will heat more quickly than the detector, the operating element in the detector will usually be at a slightly lower temperature than the surrounding air. This difference in temperature is referred to as thermal lag and could in some circumstances delay a detector's response. Its extent will depend on a number of factors e.g. the surface area of a detector, the amount and speed of air passing the device.

This is however an important point to be borne in mind when deciding on the desirable operating temperature for 'fixed temperature' detectors.

Chapter 14
Automatic fire detectors—some developments

1 The laser beam

Efforts have been made over recent years to develop the laser beam as a fire detector. A brief explanation, in simple terms, is given below.

A laser beam can be of visible or infra-red light. It has a unique advantage in that it provides a coherent band of light i.e. it does not diffuse or fan out as it travels.

The initial concept of a laser beam detection system is shown in Fig. 14.1.

Fig. 14.1 Laser fire detection system.

The beam is thrown across the protected area, fairly close to ceiling level, to fall on a photo-electric cell. In the event of fire the turbulence caused by the hot rising air produces a 'dancing' effect in the beam. The photocell is designed to react to this and raise the alarm.

The photocell is usually fronted with a checker board mask which makes it easier to discriminate between 'dancing' due to normal vibration and the more rapid 'dancing' arising from a fire condition.

In practice there were disadvantages with the initial system, not least of which was the fact that building movement could misalign it. As a result of further research and development an infra-red beam fire detection system has been devised.

The system consists essentially of an infra-red emitter unit and a separate receiver unit (see Plates 25, 26 and 27). The two units are mounted at opposite ends of the space to be protected, the distance between them being up to 90/100 metres. They are usually mounted close to ceiling level. The emitter unit sends out a low power pulsed infra-red beam, and the receiver unit is tuned to accept the pulsed frequency. Critical alignment between the two units is not necessary because the beam of radiation is relatively wide.

The plume of hot gas rising from beneath the beam (or up to 6 metres either side of it) causes modulation of the pulsed beam, at a characteristic frequency, and this is filtered out and gives a fire signal in the receiver unit (Fig. 14.2).

Because of this filtering facility a checker-board mask is no longer necessary.

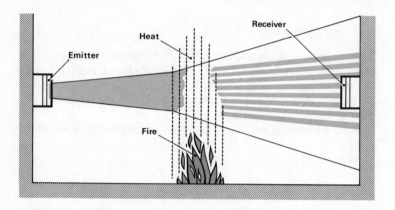

Fig. 14.2 Effect of flame on an infra-red beam detector.

The unit serves also as a very sensitive smoke detector, because a separate circuit responds to obscuration of the light beam, and is made to give a separate smoke warning. The equipment is thus sensitive to both heat and smoke conditions.

Close interruption of the beam, or failure of the radiation source, results in a fault warning.

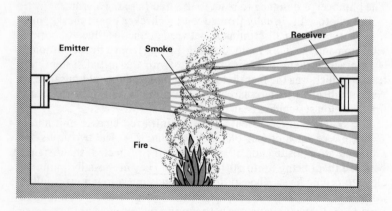

Fig. 14.3 Effect of smoke on infra-red beam detector.

This development is likely to fill a valuable place in the protection of large factory and warehouse spaces with high ceilings, where other forms of detection are difficult to provide and limited in their effectiveness.

2 General

Although the basic principles of automatic fire detection remain the same, it will be appreciated from descriptions in previous chapters that they have a variety of applications. Many further developments are taking place in this sphere. Small electromagnets are being incorporated in smoke detectors to provide a heat detection element, thus producing a dual purpose detector. Transistorised and integrated circuits are being used more widely—producing more compact and, in some cases, more sophisticated detectors.

Chapter 15
Automatic fire detectors—a summary

A summary is produced on the following pages providing an easy reference to the suitability and main points of smoke, radiation and heat detectors.

This is followed by a brief guide to detector selection and some of the principles contributing to effective detection.

Acknowledgement is made to the technical publications *The Fire Journal* and the *Fire Surveyor* from which information contained in the summary and the amalgam in Fig. 15.1 were derived.

1 The summary

Types and summary of main points

Suitability

SMOKE

a Ionisation
Sensitive in the early stages of a fire when smoke particles are small. Sensitivity tends to drop as particles grow in size.

b Optical
Most effective in situations where the protected risk is likely to give rise to dense smoke (i.e. large particles).

Areas having a controlled environment i.e. free from airborne dust etc. and generally housing complex equipment of a high intrinsic value e.g. computer installations. Normally used as point detectors but have been developed to form zone sampling systems—by monitoring air samples drawn through tubes.

RADIATION

a Infra-red
Rapid detection because of almost instantaneous transmission of radiation to the detector head. This is dependent, however, on the detector having a clear 'view' of all parts of the protected area.

b Ultra-violet
As for infra-red.

Warehouses or storage areas etc. Detectors are available which can scan large open areas and will respond only to the distinctive flame flicker. Can be used to detect certain chemical fires. The ultra-violet detector tends to be used mainly for specialised purposes.

Types and summary of main points	Suitability

HEAT

a Fusible alloys
Alloy will need replacing each time detector operates.

b Expansion of metal, air, and liquid.
Generally self re-setting.

c Electrical effect
Not widely installed—some specialist use.

Note for all types of heat detectors
May be used as point or line detectors and are designed to operate at a pre-selected temperature ('Fixed temperature' type) or on a rapid rise in temperature ('Rate-of-rise' type) or both. With all heat detectors (particularly fixed temp. types) 'thermal lag' needs to be considered when choosing the operating temperature.

Areas of general risk where vapour/particles are normally present. Cost is relatively low compared to other types of detectors.
   Both 'fixed temp.' and 'rate-of-rise' are equally efficient—but:—'Fixed temperature' types are preferred in areas where a rapid rise in temperature is a likely result of the normal work processes.
   'Rate-of-rise' types will compensate for gradual rises in ambient temperature and are more efficient than the 'fixed temperature' type in low temperature situations.
   (As mentioned in the text (page 117) 'rate-of-rise' detectors generally incorporate a fixed temperature device.)

2 Detector selection—type of detector

It is clear from the earlier table that although all available types of detector will, in the main, detect a fire, not all will be equally sensitive in every possible situation. In some cases a combination of various detectors may be required.

In general terms, smoke and heat detectors are suitable for most buildings. Radiation detectors are particularly useful for high-roofed buildings, e.g. warehouses, etc., and situations in which clean burning flammable liquids are kept.

Little experience is available at the present time on laser/infra-red beam detectors but they appear to have advantages where there are tall compartments or long cable tunnels for example.

Such generalisations, however, need to be considered in conjunction with other factors—the nature of the risk to be protected, the processes that are normally carried on and the plan of the area to be protected. These considerations enable further decisions to be made:

(a)   The reliability required from the detector

(b)   The sensitivity required from the detector

(c)   The location of detectors.

a. Detector reliability

Obviously a more robust detector is needed in an industrial setting than is required for hotel purposes. Dusty or damp atmospheres will affect some detectors more than others; (mention has previously been made of the advantage of mercury switches in this type of situation. Micro-switches can be even more reliable).

b. Detector sensitivity

This is an important consideration. It would obviously be un-desirable to install a smoke detector set at high sensitivity in a normally crowded hotel bar (or similar conditions).

In this connection it is interesting to note that in research into false alarms from automatic fire detection systems the greatest percentage of false alarms (17.5 per cent) were due to extraneous heat

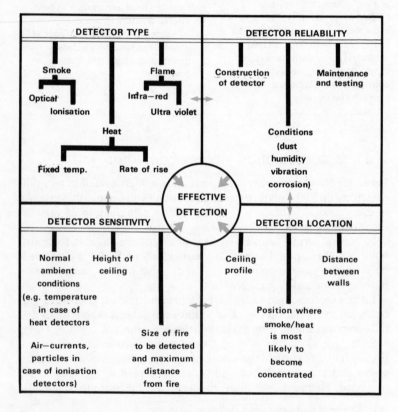

Fig. 15.1 Aspects needing consideration relative to detector selection.
(Note : To be fully effective detectors must be part of an efficient and reliable system which will include power supplies, signalling facilities and control and indicating equipment. These aspects are dealt with in Chapters 17 and 18.)

and smoke in the ambient conditions. To quote from the report*
'This could arise from carelessness within the premises, from unfore-
seen circumstances or from insufficient attention being paid to the
conditions by the designers and installers of the system'.

c. Detector location

The Fire Offices' Committee rules and the British Standard 5839
Pt. 1 lay down certain rules governing the spacing of detectors.
These rules are for guidance and while the maximum recommended
spacing should never be exceeded it is important that the rules are
thoughtfully applied in relation to the geography of the area to be
protected—having regard to its shape etc. The detectors should be
so located that they are in the best possible position to perform
their function.

Conclusion

If proper consideration is given to these various factors a more
effective detection system is likely to result. No hard and fast rules
can be drawn up on detector selection however. In the final analysis
it needs to be based on experience and a careful assessment of all the
known factors pertaining to the protected area.

Fig. 15.1 provides a summary of the main points to be considered
relative to detector selection.

---

* Fire Research Note No. 810. March 1970

Chapter 16
Manually-operated fire alarms

In the introduction to Part 2 (page 87) the point was made that a fire alarm can be raised automatically by a detection system or manually by a person in the affected building. This chapter examines the means available to a person in the affected building for raising an alarm. These means will generally be either manual or manual/electric, not forgetting that an alarm can always be raised vocally!

1 Manual systems

The purely manual means for raising an alarm involve the use of basic devices which include the following:

(i)   Rotary gongs (see Plate 28) which are sounded by simply leading the handle around the rim of the gong

(ii)   Hand strikers e.g. iron triangles suspended from a wall accompanied by a metal bar which is used to strike the triangle and produce a loud clanging noise

(iii)   Handbells

(iv)   Whistles.

These devices are normally found on the walls of corridors, entrance halls and staircase landings—in a situation where they are readily available to anyone who may need to raise an alarm.

It is, of course, relatively cheap to provide these devices. While they give an alarm over a limited area, operation of one of them is rarely adequate to give a general alarm throughout the premises; nor do they necessarily convey the alarm to a central point from which the fire brigade can be speedily summoned.

As a person is required to operate them a continuous alarm cannot be guaranteed for as long as may be necessary.

Because of these restrictions in their use it is unlikely (and in certain instances undesirable) that these devices will be the sole means of raising alarms except perhaps in low risk areas.

2 Manual/electric systems

These are systems which, although set in motion manually, operate as part of an electrical alarm circuit. Manual call points can, in fact, be incorporated with detectors into a comprehensive fire alarm system which allows for automatic and/or manual raising of an alarm.

The call points in a manual/electric system are invariably small, wall mounted boxes as shown in Plate 29. They are designed to operate either:

(i) automatically, when the glass front is broken

    or

(ii) when the glass front is broken AND the button push pressed in.

The majority of available models are designed to operate immediately the glass front is broken.

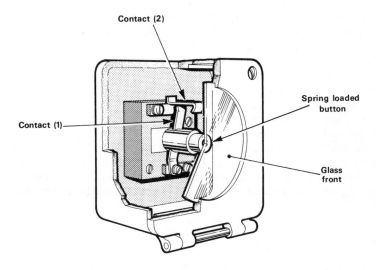

Fig. 16.1 A basic illustration of a fire-alarm call point.

Contact (1) (Fig. 16.1) is connected to one side of the electrical circuit, contact (2) is connected to the other side. The movement of contact (1) is governed by the spring loaded button which is maintained in position by the glass front. In the healthy situation contact (1) is therefore held off contact (2), but once the glass is broken, the spring forces the spring-loaded button outwards, allowing contact (1) to engage with contact (2) thus completing the electrical circuit and raising the alarm.

As an alternative this type of call-point can be fitted so that the electrical circuit is complete in the healthy state, a relay being incorporated to hold off the alarm. On breaking the glass the circuit is broken, the relay de-energises and the alarm sounds.

In either case, accidental breaking of the glass will, of course, raise a false alarm. This is most likely to happen in a situation where various goods and materials are being moved about (e.g. in workshops and storage areas). In these situations the problem can be overcome by installing a call-point in which the push button has to be manually pressed in to raise the alarm after the glass has been broken (Plate 30).

To help with the breaking of the glass in call points most manufacturers will provide, if requested, a small chromium-plated hammer for attaching by chain to the box (see Plate 31). In lieu of the hammer some manufacturers will 'score' a circle in the glass for easier breakage; in one case sufficient to be broken by a blow with the tips of the fingers.

Obviously these arrangements are desirable only when the possibility of accidental or malicious breaking is minimal.

Where neither hammer nor scored glass is available a blow with a covered elbow, a shoe heel or other sharp object will be effective.

In certain types of occupancy (e.g. mental hospitals) or in situations where vandalism is likely, a modified call point is often fitted. It can be seen from Plate 32 that these points have a solid door with a keyhole. When the key is inserted and turned the electric circuit is completed and an alarm is raised.

The key will normally be in the possession of, or accessible to, authorised personnel only.

Recommendations on the installation of manual call points are given in British Standard 5839 Pt. 1. In general terms they should obviously be fitted in conspicuous positions, usually on escape routes, where anyone operating them is not exposed to undue risk.

3 Miscellaneous

In addition to the facilities specifically designed for raising an alarm it is possible to use facilities which may already be installed in a building for other purposes, e.g. a telephone or public address system.

With automatic telephone systems arrangements can be made for a particular dialling code to be reserved for use when reporting a fire. Use of such a code can connect the caller to a person (normally the operator) responsible for calling the fire brigade and sounding the general alarm; alternatively it can be arranged that use of the code automatically sounds the general alarm.

While such systems are useful as 'back-up' services it can be unwise to rely on them as the sole means of raising an alarm. They have two main disadvantages.

(i)   Delay—the delay that can occur between the person detecting the fire contacting the person at the switchboard or public address system; the further delay that can occur between this contact and the actual raising of the general alarm.

(ii) Familiarity (particularly with a public address or manual telephone system)—the fact that people are familiar with these systems being used for other purposes may mean that they treat them with less urgency than deserved when they are used as fire alarms.

4 Restricted alarms

In order to avoid unnecessary disturbance in hospitals and other large installations it may be desirable to restrict an initial alarm to the locality in which it arises or restrict it to a small number of responsible personnel. A general alarm would then be sounded only if a 'duty officer' considered it desirable to do so.

Signal light systems which are often installed for summoning staff for various purposes, can be used for restricted alarms; operation of the call point producing a certain light code signal. These lights are installed at ward entrances (in the case of hospitals), at passage intersections and other places where they are conspicuous to staff.

Restricted alarm systems must have a control point which is under continuous and competent watch during the whole time the premises are occupied. An overriding switch should also be provided to enable the 'duty officer' or other responsible person to raise a general alarm for complete evacuation.

If an alarm is to be restricted it will also be necessary to have some supplementary means of summoning fire-fighting staff to the affected area.

Chapter 17
Automatic fire detection—detector circuits

The function of the detector circuit in an automatic detection system is to transmit the signal given by the activated detector head (or manual call point) to centrally situated control and indicating equipment from which the alarm is raised. In practice these processes occur simultaneously.

Basically there are two types of detector circuit:

(1) 'Open' circuit

(2) 'Closed' circuit

their condition being reversed in each case to raise the alarm.

1 'Open' circuit—the theory

In an 'open' circuit system detectors or call points are wired in parallel and can be regarded as switches in the 'off' position i.e. there is no current flow in the circuit when on standby. The operation of a detector effectively closes the contacts and activates the alarm system.

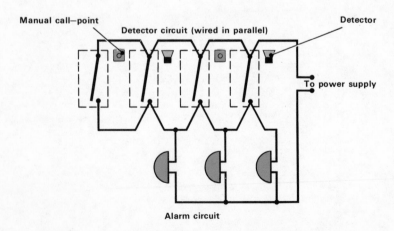

Fig. 17.1 Diagram of an 'open' circuit system.

As there is no current flow in the circuit when on standby it is not self monitoring; as a result however it does not consume as much electricity as a 'closed' circuit and is therefore relatively cheaper to run. A short circuit in the detector wiring will raise an alarm, as it effectively closes the circuit. A broken circuit on the other hand will not and if unidentified could render some detector heads inoperative.

It is important to remember that in all except the simplest systems the detector and alarm circuits are separate—meeting only in the alarm control unit (for simplicity this has been omitted from Figs. 17.1 and 17.2).

2 'Closed' circuit—the theory

In a 'closed' circuit the detectors (or call points) can be regarded as a series of switches whose contacts are normally closed when the system is on standby thus allowing current to flow in the detector circuit. This current energises the relay which holds contact (1) (Fig. 17.2) against contact (3) and keeps the alarm circuit inoperative. Once a detector (or call point) operates the detector circuit is broken interrupting current flow to the relay.

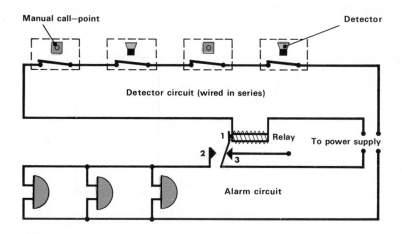

Fig. 17.2 Diagram of a 'closed' circuit system.

The relay is therefore de-energised releasing contact (1) which springs back to contact (2), completing the alarm circuit and sounding the bells.

The main advantage of this type of circuit is that the continuous current flow on standby makes it self monitoring. Any break in the circuit will cause the alarm to ring; which, although it may be false, does at least draw attention to the fault. The fact that the circuit is drawing current from the supply on standby however can be regarded as a disadvantage—the size and cost of the battery and charger will be increased. In a basic 'closed' circuit system a short circuit could remain unnoticed as it simply completes a separate path for current flow. In doing this it could by-pass some detectors and call points rendering them inoperative.

3 Detector and alarm circuits—the practice

It is essential that detector and alarm circuits are above all reliable. The diagrams in Figs. 17.1 and 17.2 are basic illustrations of 'open' and 'closed' circuits. In practice the circuitry, although based on 'open' and 'closed' principles, is more sophisticated than this. Ring circuits and other refinements can be used to achieve, as far as possible, a fail-safe situation and to overcome the disadvantage mentioned earlier. Resistors and/or additional relays are incorporated to reduce false alarms by providing for separate signalling of fault conditions (e.g. a broken circuit or a short circuit).

Closed circuits have the advantage mentioned earlier that they are continuously under test i.e. current flows in the circuit on standby. If desired, however, the continuity of an 'open' circuit can be tested by incorporating an end-of-line resistor in the circuit (Fig. 17.3).

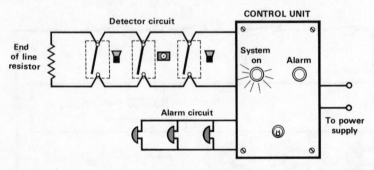

Fig. 17.3 An 'open' circuit system with end-of-line resistor.

This allows a continuous but reduced current to flow through the detector circuit. The continuity of the flow will be monitored at the control unit. The resistor incorporated in the circuit reduces the current sufficiently to prevent it activating the alarms.

The more components there are introduced into a circuit of course, the more there is to fail. With this in mind the British Standard Code of Practice 1019 states 'In the interests of reliability it is desirable that the number of circuit elements in the system . . . should be kept to a minimum. . . . Every additional component will inevitably add some risk. Nevertheless with care taken to minimise these a fully discriminating system can be well justified'. Indeed the Fire Offices' Committee rules require some element of discrimination (e.g. fault signalling or end-of-line testing) in approved systems.

Some detectors and manual call points can be used in either 'open' or 'closed' circuit systems.

4 Wiring and power supplies

a. Wiring

It is essential for reliability that the wiring in automatic fire alarm systems should be of a high standard and be suitably protected against the possibility of accidental damage. The degree of protection needed in an 'open' circuit will generally be greater than that needed in a 'closed' circuit in which any break in the wiring will automatically sound an alarm.

The thermostatic cable described on page 110 can be used for wiring detector circuits—it is mainly used wuth heat detectors.

b. Power supplies

Obviously an adequate and reliable power supply must be available to automatic detection systems.

This can be a mains supply or a battery supply. In either case it is advisable (Fire Offices' Committee rules require) that a standby supply must be automatically available in the event of a failure in the primary supply. The standby supply will normally be a battery maintained in a fully-charged state. This supply can be automatically brought into operation by incorporating a changeover relay in the circuit.

The preferred operating voltage is 24 V d.c. A transformer will therefore be necessary to reduce the voltage to installations using a mains supply.

Chapter 18
Control and indicating equipment

The two main components of the equipment are:

(i)   the control unit

(ii) the indicator panel.

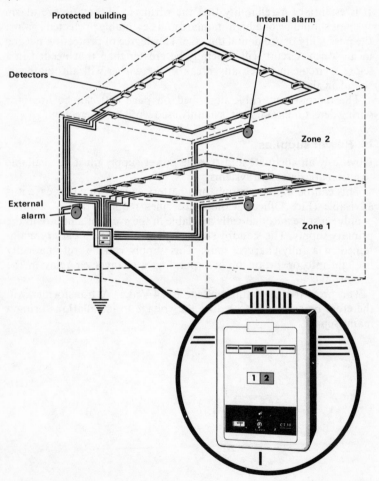

Fig. 18.1 Diagram of an automatic fire detection and alarm system with enlarged inset of a control unit/indicator panel.

The control unit acts as a terminal for the detector and alarm circuits.

It houses the components which control the operation of the internal and external alarms; where appropriate these components will transmit the alarm signal to the fire brigade. It is common for the unit also to house test facilities, alarm silence button, alarm reset button and fault signalling facilities.

In a real sense the control unit is the nerve centre of the complete installation (Fig. 18.1).

The prime function of the control unit is to initiate an alarm when a detector or call point is operated.

Some control units incorporate a system known as 'latching'. In this system the alarm relay controls the alarm contact AND a 'latching' contact.

When a detector is actuated both of these contacts close forming a current path which is confined within the control unit (Fig. 18.2). This path supplies current to the alarm circuit. As it is within the protection of the control unit the alarms will continue to sound even if the detector wiring is damaged as a result of the developing fire situation.

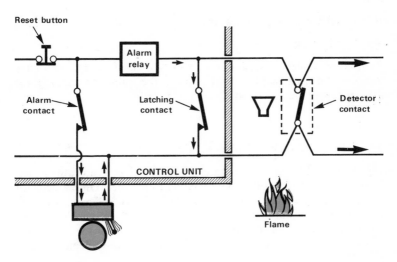

Fig. 18.2 Diagram of 'latching'.

This is obviously a desirable feature particularly in 'open' circuits. Even intermittent faults will cause continuous ringing of the bells. As the system can only be reset after the cause of the alarm has been dealt with, faults are unlikely to go unnoticed. (Resetting can normally be achieved using the reset button or switch on the control and indicating equipment.)

In many buildings it will be necessary for the location of any fire to be known at some central point; for this purpose control units normally include an indicator panel (Fig. 18.1). Hence the composite term 'control and indicating equipment'.

The indicator panel will show at a glance the approximate location of the part of the premises for which the alarm has sounded. This is achieved by dividing the system into zones, each zone of the protected building having its own group of detectors. These may be allocated on the basis of floors or self-contained areas within the protected building, depending on what are considered as desirable and practicable zones from a fire protection and fire-fighting point of view taking into account size and accessibility. The British Standard Code of Practice stipulates that no zone should extend beyond one floor.

Each group of detectors will be connected to a separate zone indicator on the indicator panel. The number of zone indicators on the panel therefore will depend on the number of floors or departments in a building.

Most control and indicating equipment will give audible warning of fire; the type of visual signal given will depend on the indicator panel chosen. Broadly, there are two types of visual signalling available:

(i)   Drop flag (or flap) indicators

(ii) Luminous indicators.

Luminous indicators are the more widely used of the two and have therefore been chosen for description in the following pages: three different types are described.

1 Luminous indicator—type 1

Fig. 18.3 (and Plate 33) illustrates a basic luminous indicator panel/ control unit, capable of accommodating four zones. Once a detector or call point is actuated the indicator lamp for the affected zone will be illuminated simultaneously with the raising of the alarm. The advantage of visual signalling is that it allows for rapid indentification of the affected zone and should help in efficient deployment of local and brigade resources to that area.

In common with most control and indicating equipment this model has an alarm silence button. By pushing this button ringing alarm bells can be silenced. The lamp(s) will remain illuminated and cannot be reset until the actuated detectors or call points have been restored to normal. A safeguard is thereby provided against detectors being left inoperative.

The use of an alarm silence button does not prevent a further alarm sounding should the fire condition subsequently spread to other zones. (The button resets itself immediately after use). Where bells are silenced using an alarm silence button, an audible alarm can be maintained on a supervisory buzzer. This can be fitted in or adjacent to the control unit and acts as a further reminder that the system remains in an alarm condition and should be reset as soon as practicable. It also has the advantage of reducing current consumption to a minimum while maintaining an audible alarm.

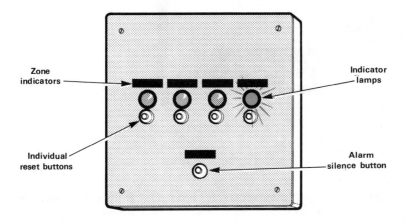

Fig. 18.3 Basic luminous indicator panel/control unit.

Some of these smaller luminous indicator panels/control units are not capable of automatically signalling fault conditions as required by British Standard 3116 and the Fire Offices' Committee rules.

2 Luminous indicator—type 2

The indicator panel/control unit illustrated in Fig. 18.4 (and Plate 34) is a little more sophisticated than type 1. In practice further identification of the affected zone can be provided by either fixed name plates above each zone number or having an annotated plan of the protected area adjacent to the panel, as shown in Plate 35.

As well as the facilities described for type 1 this equipment (Fig. 18.4), incorporates indicators which show the state of the system and, in accordance with British Standard 3116, it is capable of signalling both visually and audibly either a 'fire' or 'fault' condition. The visual signal for fire is red and for fault, amber.

Further refinements on this particular model include a testing facility and key switches for zone isolation. The isolation switches allow individual zones (or the complete system) to be switched off for

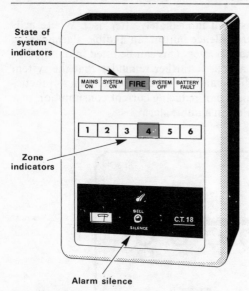

Fig. 18.4 Luminous indicator panel/control unit.

maintenance purposes. Where this is done the British Standard 3116 requires some visual indication to be shown on the indicator panel.

3 Luminous indicator—type 3 (plan indicator)

A plan indicator may be desirable when a system covers a large and perhaps complex area. These indicators have a plan of the protected area engraved or fixed on the indicator panel. Miniature lamps, each representing a specific zone, are set in or behind the plan and are illuminated automatically when a detector is activated, showing the location of the fire at a glance.

4 Signal selection unit

Where a detection and alarm system is connected to the Brigade's VF system A, a signal selection unit (Plate 36) may be fitted at the protected premises in addition to a control unit/indicator panel.

As can be seen from Plate 36 the signal selection unit serves three main functions:

(i)   it confirms that the signal has been transmitted to the brigade (top left—red);

(ii) it receives an acknowledgement signal when 'a key' is operated by Control room staff (top right—green);

(iii) it provides facilities for testing the connection to the brigade (centre).

Once the unit has signalled a fire condition it has to be manually reset before it will operate again.

A similar unit may be fitted when the connection is to the alarm company's own central control room.

Details and an explanation of the various facilities for transmitting automatic fire alarms to brigades or other centres are given in the *Manual of Firemanship, Book 10, 'Fire brigade communications'*.

Indicator panels/control units—conclusion

The indicator panels/control units described above represent the three main types available. They also serve to illustrate the basic functions required from such equipment—rapid identification of the affected zone and facilities for fault signalling and testing. The main methods used for circuit testing on the equipment are switches, press buttons or jack plugs.

A wide variety of control and indicating equipment is available from a simple switch and relay arrangment to large consoles with sophisticated electronic equipment—all planned to cater for differing situations. What is important is that all indicator panels in particular should be so designed that any person responding to an alarm can easily and correctly read the visual signal being given.

As far as the siting of the control and indicating equipment is concerned the British Standard Code of Practice states:

'The position of the fire alarm system's control and indicating equipment should be carefully chosen having due regard to operational requirements and preferably in areas of low risk. For example, both control and indicator panels should at all times be accessible from within the building and therefore should not be sited in any area which is at times locked up. It is often advantageous if the indicator panel is visible from outside the buildings.

In any case the equipment should be near the entrance normally used by the fire brigade or any other persons responding to an alarm. If necessary its position should be emphasised by indicator or direction signs'.

F

Part 3
Fire venting systems

Practical fire venting is referred to in the *Manual of Firemanship,* Book 12. This Part of *Fire Protection of Buildings,* however, examines ventilation systems which are a structural part of a building. For the purposes of this Manual they are considered in two groups.

1 Single-storey buildings

The main advantages of fire venting systems in single storey buildings are two fold—the reduction of fire spread and the prevention of smoke logging; both of which make it possible for firemen to enter a building to control a fire. These fitted ventilation systems sometimes double as both health and fire ventilation.

2 Multi-storey buildings

In this case the ventilation systems are generally installed for health purposes and in fire conditions can prove a hazard rather than a help. The chapter on 'Ventilation and air conditioning systems' describes the fire prevention measures designed to control the potential hazard of such systems.

Chapter 19
Ventilation in single-storey buildings

In fire conditions it is generally accepted that correct ventilation reduces fire spread and resultant damage, and also enables firemen to enter the building more easily. In many of the large single-storey factories in this country there are large open production areas with unprotected roof trussing and few (if any) interior walls. These buildings often house material or processes with high fire risks. Ventilation systems have been successfully introduced to such buildings minimising the spread of fire and reducing heavy losses.

1 Purpose of venting

The purpose of venting is basically three fold:

(a) to facilitate fire fighting

(b) to prevent the spread of fire

(c) to reduce damage by heat and smoke.

a. Fire fighting

Venting allows smoke and other products of combustion to leave the building making a cool, clear atmosphere at ground level (Fig. 19.1). The increased visibility enables firemen to locate the seat of the fire.

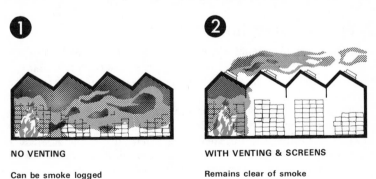

NO VENTING

Can be smoke logged
within 5 minutes of outbreak

WITH VENTING & SCREENS

Remains clear of smoke
until extinguished

Fig. 19.1 Adequate venting allows combustion products to leave the building. The effect: (1) with no venting; (2) with venting and screens.

Smoke logging can be prevented by early venting which provides added oxygen for more complete combustion. This is most easily achieved by an automatically controlled system. In a small building the effect is immediate in the early stages of a fire, while in a large building it is only as the fire develops that venting provides the oxygen necessary for complete combustion.

Besides preventing smoke logging automatic controls are also favoured because:

(i) there may be problems in reaching manual controls in fire conditions

(ii) they provide the possibility of earlier detection since the smoke may be seen by passers by.

b. Spread of fire

Mushrooming (the high level spread of hot gases and smoke) is also checked by early ventilation. This prevents the pre-heating of other areas by convection, thereby restricting the spread of fire.

Ventilation also reduces the area of roof damage away from the fire by restricting the sideways spread of flames beneath the ceiling. Damage is greater over the fire area but proportionally less at a distance from the fire.

c. Damage reduction

Attacking the blaze and preventing the spread of fire obviously reduces the damage done by heat and smoke. For example, the release of heat obviously reduces the temperature of the roof. Distortion and softening of the steel framework (which occurs at approximately 500°C) are avoided, preventing the collapse of the walls.

The release of the products of combustion also eliminates the explosion risk of partially burnt gases.

2 Specific use of fire ventilators

Ventilators fitted in buildings may well vent the products of combustion when there is a fire. The ventilators examined in this chapter, however, are those fitted to buildings *primarily* for fire venting purposes.

Some vents are designed for the dual role of fire and health ventilation. When used for health purposes, ventilators are ganged together in groups and operated by mechanically or pneumatically controlled systems. Under fire conditions the ventilators are liberated from the control system to operate individually.

3 Vent construction

Most vents are designed with opening doors or pivoted louvres.

Some examples of these can be seen in Plates 37, 38, 39. Steel or reinforced polyester resin is used for the doors, while louvres are generally made of aluminium. The opening mechanism is operated by a fire detector of some kind. (There is further information on fire detectors later in this chapter).

Vents made from polythene based plastics do not have a separate fire detector. The vent itself is made of plastic which has a relatively low melting point (about 300°C). When softened by heat the sheet of plastic falls from its mounting leaving the vent open.

4 Vent operation

Both heat and smoke detectors are used for automatic vent control.

a. Heat detectors

The simplest and most common method of detection used is the fusible link. The time for reaction depends on its size, shape, material and position. The link is usually shielded from sprinkler discharge so that water does not delay its action (Fig. 19.2).

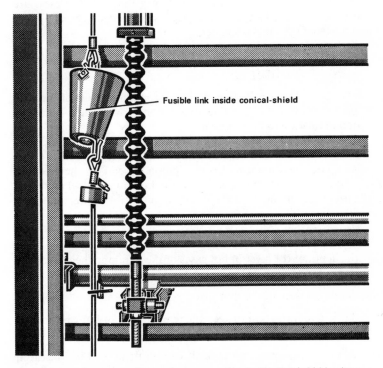

Fusible link inside conical-shield

Fig. 19.2 Part of a roof ventilator—louvre type. The fusible link is hidden by a conical shield preventing water cooling.

b. Smoke detectors

These are used as a back-up to fusible links in very high buildings. Heat rising a great height may cool so that fusing temperatures are not reached but when smoke has collected in the roof smoke detectors will operate instead.

5 Vent position

Vent efficiency is largely dependent on site. Vents should ideally be at the highest point in each control area, usually the apex. Vents are sited so that the suction effect produced by the wind aids the flow of hot gases.

Sometimes the pressure on windward slopes with steep pitches tends to force cold air into the building producing smoke logging. For these difficult positions roof ventilators have been designed with electrically driven fans to overcome the air pressure. Wiring, switch-gear and motors have to be specially designed to withstand severe heating.

It is generally advantageous to substitute one large vent by a number of small ones distributed evenly over the roof. The exposure hazard to other buildings is decreased since the height of flames emerging from the vents is smaller.

6 Area of venting

If vents have a lower softening temperature than the rest of the roof e.g. plastic roof vents, Building Regulations govern their area and position in relation to the boundary.

Vents which have equal ability to resist fire as the rest of the roof however are not covered separately by Building Regulations. In this case estimated requirements for ventilation depend on the assumed size of the fire rather than the size of the building. Calculations for ventilation requirements depend on a number of interconnected variables:

(i)   the assumed size of the fire

(ii) the depth of the layer of hot gases or the minimum height for the layer of cool clear air

(iii) the subdivision of the roof space

(iv) the general intention to keep the temperature of hot gases below approximately 200°C.

This subject is complex and is dealt with in detail in Fire Research Technical Paper No. 10 '*Design of Roof Venting Systems for Single Storey Buildings*'.

7 Air inlets

So far ventilation has only been considered as the exhaustion of the products of combustion. In fact it is the provision of adequate inlets which dictates the efficiency of any ventilation system.

Cold air generally flows into the building by natural means—leaks round doors, windows and other apertures. These inlets must be below the expected level of hot air and ideally as near the floor as possible. If the inlets are not low enough cold air may entrain hot gases and result in smoke logging at ground level.

It is recommended that the area of air inlets should at least equal the total area of roof vents. A higher ratio is desirable for premises housing goods which cause smoky fires without reaching high temperatures.

8 Other factors

In reality it is impossible to consider ventilation in isolation. There are several factors which influence the effectiveness of a venting system. The most important ones are:

(a) the sub division of the roof space with screens

(b) the position of sprinklers.

a. Screens

Subdividing the roof space with screens is known to considerably increase the efficiency of vents, and was mentioned as one of the factors affecting the area of ventilators required.

(1) Screen construction

Screens are constructed of material which is as resistant to the effects of fire as the roof (not necessarily non-combustible). They need to be reasonably gas-tight although small leaks where pipes pass through are not of great importance particularly when low down.

Screens are generally placed at right angles to a pitched roof (Fig. 19.3), dividing the roof into compartments.

Screens are generally fixed 45–60 metres apart. This varies according to the factory or storage layout since screens positioned over spaces between goods, tend to reduce fire spread.

It is the depth of the screens which governs the time before hot air spills into adjacent compartments. Screens should, ideally, reach as near the floor as possible to prevent fire spread by radiation. In practice they often only reach down as far as truss tie level as shown in Fig. 19.3.

Some screens are constructed so that in normal conditions they are

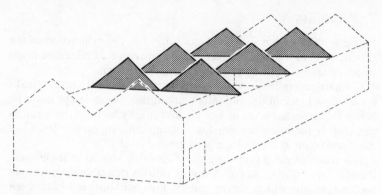

Fig. 19.3 A diagrammatic example of screens dividing a roof space.

retracted near the roof and under fire conditions they fall on operation of a fusible link (Fig. 19.4).

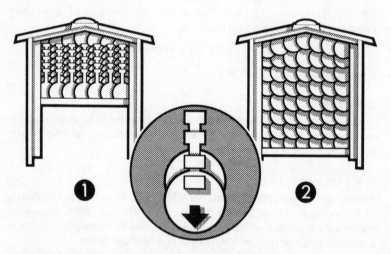

Fig. 19.4 The operation of screens (1) normal conditions (2) under fire conditions; (inset) shows in more detail the function of the screens.

(2) Screen effect

If a roof is divided into compartments by screens the area above the fire fills first. The local temperature is increased and this significantly improves the response time of automatic roof vents.

The lateral flow of smoke is restricted so that roof vents in a non smoke-logged part of the building can be opened to allow the air to flow (Fig. 19.5).

When used in conjunction with sprinklers screens restrict water damage by preventing the activation of sprinkler heads away from the source of the fire.

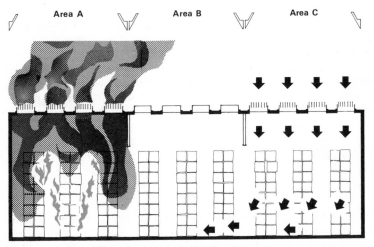

WAREHOUSE BUILDING WITH LIMITED DOOR OPENING.

When fire vents over Area C are opened cool air falls to the floor, drifts towards the fire and allows vents over the hot area to exhaust at full capacity.
System maintains safe condition for fire fighting and avoids unnecessary damage by smoke and blind use of water.

Fig. 19.5 A warehouse with limited door opening—lateral flow restriction being reduced by opening of vents in a cool area.

b. Sprinklers

Sprinklers themselves influence the effectiveness of a ventilation system. There is much debate as to whether sprinklers or ventilators should operate first.

If sprinklers operate *before* vents, rising gases and smoke may be cooled, thus increasing vent opening times and at worst causing them not to operate at all.

If sprinklers operate *after* vents, the escaping heat may retard their early operation. However this does restrict the opening of sprinklers away from the fire, which in turn obviously prevents unnecessary water damage.

The opinion held currently puts the operation of sprinkler heads first. This cuts out the possibility of vent operation delaying the opening of sprinklers and ensures that the fire area is adequately covered by a sprinkler attack prior to venting. This may, however, result in the operation of some sprinklers away from the fire.

9 Additional controls

In some fire situations e.g. smouldering, it may be desirable to open fire vents before the temperature for automatic operation is reached. To cater for this many installations have 'Fireman's Override Controls' fixed in positions agreed with the local fire brigade (often near a sprinkler stop valve or other control point) (see Plate 40). This control switch opens all vents connected to it and overrides any other controls in the system.

Some installations have a built-in safeguard against vents used for general ventilation being carelessly left open in rain. A rain-sensing device operates an electro-pneumatic valve which causes all vents to shut until the rain has ceased (Plate 41). A fireman would fail to open fire vents by the normal control valves if it were raining or if hoses were playing near the rain-sensing panel. He must use the override switch.

10 Special venting problems

In the 60's the importance of preserving smoke free escape routes in large shopping complexes was recognised. Smoke from a shop on fire in a covered mall must find quick exit from the mall roof. This demands a relatively large number of small ventilators to give a wide distribution.

Because the vents will be in an area not directly above the fire they may not receive enough heat to open them until a considerable volume of smoke has flowed along the mall. Smoke sensing actuators are desirable in such cases.

This subject is dealt with in considerable detail in *Fire Prevention Guide No. 1*, '*Fire precautions in town centre developments*'.

Conclusion

Automatic ventilation systems have proved invaluable in restricting the spread of fire and therefore damage. Ventilation releases the smoke, heat and gases which generally cause the fireman greatest difficulty. It also makes unnecessary the danger of breaking open parts of a building to relieve smoke logging.

Chapter 20
Ventilation and air-conditioning systems

Automatic fire venting as described in the previous chapter is not generally applicable to multi-storey buildings. Although it is possible to treat the top storey as though it were a single-storey and install automatic roof vents, they would have limited application—perhaps to vent smoke from lift shafts in a fire situation.

However the use of health venting and air-conditioning systems in multi-storey buildings is increasing. The complexity of any system will, of course, vary in relation to such factors as, the building structure, the number of employees, and the work processes being carried on. In all cases, such systems can present a hazard rather than a help in an outbreak of fire.

Fire prevention measures have therefore been devised in an attempt to control the potential fire hazard of these systems.

This chapter describes these measures, including the associated topic of staircase pressurisation. Such measures are designed to fulfil a similar purpose in multi-storey buildings as automatic roof vents achieve in single-storey buildings. That is:

(i)   to prevent the spread of fire

(ii) to facilitate fire-fighting

(iii) to reduce damage by smoke and heat.

In the case of multi-storey buildings they fulfil a further and important function:

(iv) to keep means of escape smoke and fire free.

1   Systems used

As described in the *Manual of Firemanship, Book 8, Building construction and structural fire protection*, mechanical ventilation systems may be divided into three main groups; those in which:

(i)   vitiated air is extracted by fans (fresh air finding its way in through windows and doors)—known as 'exhaust' ventilation

(ii) fresh air is forced in by fans (vitiated air finding its way out through windows and doors)—known as 'plenum' ventilation

(iii) fans are used to force in fresh air and extract vitiated air. This is a combination of (i) and (ii) and is known as 'balanced' ventilation.

Air conditioning is simply an extension of these systems incorporating means for warming or cooling the air, providing the right humidity and so on—in fact creating an artificial environment within a building. If such a system is to be effective and economic the building has to be 'sealed' from the outside environment, thus offering little, if any, facility for natural ventilation.

All installations have at least one plant room normally on the roof or in the basement. Large buildings may have many plant rooms, located throughout the premises but supervised from a central control room, permanently manned but readily accessible to fire service personnel responding to an incident.

2 Plant room

A plant room should be enclosed with walls or partitions having a standard of fire resistance at least equal to that required for the part of the building in which it is situated. If the room is likely to be used for other purposes in addition to housing the plant, a fire damper (see page 166) should be fitted to the main duct where it leaves the plant room.

In the case of air-conditioning plant, oil or gas may be used to warm the air, freon or other refrigerants used to cool it. These substances present a hazard in themselves and as a precaution the British Standard Code of Practice 3, Chapter IV, recommends the installation of a fire detection system which would automatically close down the plant in a fire situation. The type of detector to be used should be carefully chosen in relation to the risk being protected.

Another relevant component of ventilation systems from the fire hazard viewpoint are air filters. Normally situated in the plant room their function is to reduce the dust content of incoming air. There are three main types of filter used:

(a) Dry filter

(b) Viscous filter

(c) Electrostatic filter.

a. Dry filter

In this filter, cotton wool, cloth or other fibrous material is used as the filtering medium. The material should, as far as possible, be flame resistant. Any accumulation of dust or dirt on the filter will greatly increase its flammability, so regular replacement is necessary, the used filter being safely disposed of.

b. Viscous filter

The viscous filter uses an oil-coated material to trap the dust particles in the incoming air. The oil used should have a high flash point—*not less* than 177°C is recommended. As with the dry filter regular cleaning is necessary. Some means of containing any surplus oil should also be provided so that it is not carried into the system.

c. Electrostatic filter

The important aspect of this filter from a fire point of view is that it operates at high voltages. It is therefore desirable that some means is available (either manual or automatic) to halt its operation in the event of fire. In many instances it will most likely cease operation when the plant itself is shut down.

Where it is considered there is a high fire risk from filters, or expensive machinery needs protecting, it is possible to fit an automatic extinguishing system (e.g. sprinklers) inside the ducting, close to the filter. Such systems are normally activated by a smoke detector or fusible link.

3 The ducting

A system of ducting for distributing, recycling and/or extracting the air, links the plant room with the rest of the building. Steel ducting is generally used; if other materials are chosen they should be such as not to substantially increase the risk of fire spread—(the British Standard Code of Practice 3, Chapter IV, Parts 2 and 3 require that the material be non-combustible and should not readily collapse when subjected to heat).

The layout ducts for a basic air-conditioning system is shown in Fig. 20.1. In the system illustrated the branch ducts are fitted on a traditional horizontal basis.

Some systems use a modification of the arrangement as shown in Fig. 20.2. In this arrangement the branch ducts rise vertically before entering the common main duct. Structurally this arrangement is more compact and is less likely to allow a carry over of smoke in the event of fire. While smoke will rise or spread horizontally it is not so likely to descend the branch ducts.

Whatever arrangement is used however, it is the ducting which is most likely to provide the fire hazard, not only by feeding a fire with fresh air but more seriously by providing a ready channel for the spread of smoke, heat or flame throughout the building.

There are, in fact, three ways in which ventilation and air-conditioning ducts can contribute to the seriousness of a fire:

(a) Insulating material either inside or outside the ducts may be combustible;

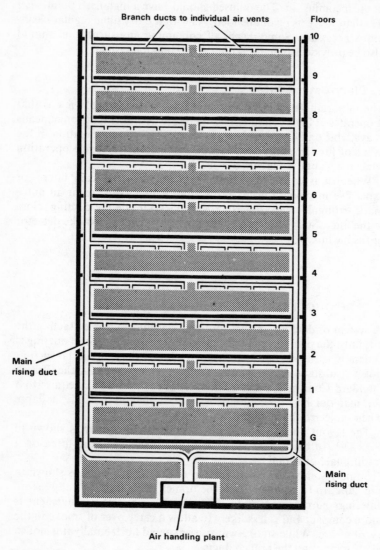

Fig. 20.1 Basic air conditioning system.

(b) Flexible joints or connections may collapse;

(c) Smoke, heat or flame may spread through the ducting.

Fire protection measures are therefore obviously necessary in these areas.

160

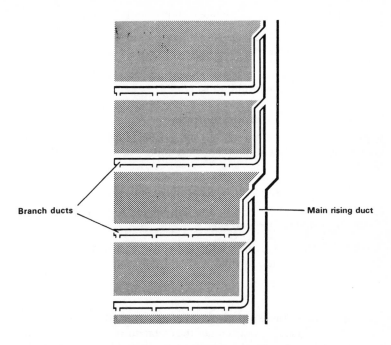

Branch ducts

Main rising duct

Fig. 20.2 Ducting system (sometimes referred to as a 'shunt' system).

a. Insulating material

From a fire prevention viewpoint it is desirable that the material used for insulating and lagging ventilation ducts should be non-combustible. Few materials, however, with this quality are suitable from a structural engineering point of view. As a result there has to be compromise in this area. The general recommendations are that combustible material used for the insulation of ducts should:

(i)   have an index of performance not exceeding 12 when tested in accordance with the propagation test in BS 476: Part 6.
      (Not more than 6 of the 12 should derive from the initial period of the test.)

(ii) generate a minimum of smoke and toxic gases when involved in a fire.

When material is tested, it is important that a representative section of the duct and its insulation is used. This allows the effects of adhesives and facings to be taken into account and thus more closely represents what will be the structural situation.

In addition to the above requirements it is recommended that:

(i)   *internal* insulating material in ducting should be no nearer than 1 metre to any fire dampers that are fitted.

(ii) *external* insulating material should not be carried through fire compartment floors and walls.

b. Flexible joints and connections

Because of the rigid nature of ducting, flexible joints and connections are used at certain points in its construction.
In brief,

(1) 'joints' are used to connect up sections of ductwork along its run

(2) 'connections' are used at the extremities to join up items of equipment (e.g. air intakes).

A feature of fires involving ventilation systems has been the collapse and destruction of these flexible joints and connections.

(1) Flexible joints

As a general rule these are used in the main duct(s) to allow for the usual contraction and expansion of the metal due to normal temperature changes. They can also prevent vibrations (from the plant for example (Fig. 20.3)) being transmitted through the complete system.

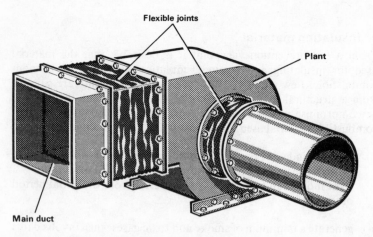

Fig. 20.3 Illustration of a flexible joint.

The collapse of a flexible joint is potentially very dangerous because this would allow fire to penetrate the main ductwork and spread throughout the building. To overcome this potential hazard there are three main recommendations in relation to installing flexible joints:

(i)   As far as practicable they should be avoided

(ii) they should not exceed 250 mm in length

(iii) they should be constructed of material which gives the minimum assistance to flame spread (i.e. Class 1 BS 476, Part 7) and which does not give off excessive quantities of smoke when burnt

(iv) they should consist of, or be protected by, materials so as to have a fire penetration time of at least 15 minutes in accordance with BS 476.

(2) Flexible connections

As shown in Fig. 20.4 these are used to connect ductwork to air intakes or ventilation grilles and generally to facilitate the site erection of fans, intake filters etc.

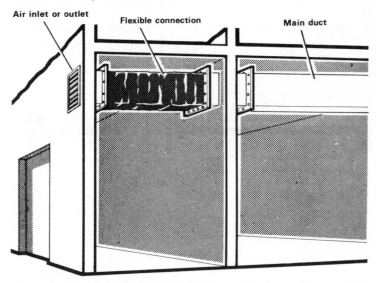

Fig. 20.4 Illustration of flexible connection.

Because of their situation at entry or exit points to the system, flexible connections do not present quite the same potential hazard. Should a fire occur in the area of a flexible connection it could enter the system via the plant (ventilation grille, fans etc.) irrespective of whether the connections collapsed or not. Nevertheless there are certain recommendations on the use of flexible connections. These are explained in Fig. 20.5.

In addition to these three points it is important that the material used in the manufacture of flexible connections should fulfil the conditions laid down for insulating material described on page 161.

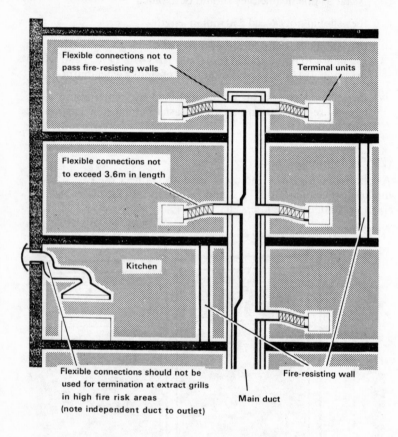

Fig. 20.5 Illustration of the use of flexible connections.

c. Smoke, heat or flame spread through ducting

If the measures already described are implemented they will go a long way towards reducing the fire hazard of ventilation and air conditioning ducts. Nevertheless the possibility of smoke, heat or flame spread through the building (via the ducting) still remains. These combustion products may not only enter the system from within the building; if air intakes are not thoughtfully sited on exterior walls smoke, heat or flame may also be drawn in from outside the building.

There are three ways in which the potential problem of smoke, heat or flame spread via ducting can be dealt with:

(1) Proper siting of air intakes

(2) Use of fire dampers in the ducts

(3) Fire stopping of shafts carrying ducts.

(1) Air intakes

As an intake draws its air from outside a building (Fig. 20.6) its position in relation to possible exterior risks needs to be considered at the installation stage. These risks can be traffic fumes, or combustion products from adjacent buildings; the risk from windows in the building itself should not be overlooked either. Flame breaking through windows could be drawn into any air intakes sited close to them. In the final analysis one is more likely to be looking for a 'minimum risk' position rather than a 'risk free' position.

Fig. 20.6 Illustration of an air intake panel.

Further protection can be obtained by fixing some form of automatic closing mechanism (e.g. fire doors or dampers) to the intake. This mechanism can be made to operate by a smoke or heat sensing device (depending on the nature of the exterior risk etc.).

Regular cleaning of any wire mesh grilles covering air intakes is a further and necessary precaution to avoid the accumulation of combustible material such as litter and dust at the system's entry point.

(2) Fire dampers

If air-conditioning and ventilation ducts pierce a fire-resisting compartment the resistance of the compartment is obviously reduced—smoke and fire have a ready means of access. Where it is necessary or desirable to maintain the integrity of a compartment in these circumstances, fire dampers can be fitted in the ducting (Fig. 20.7).

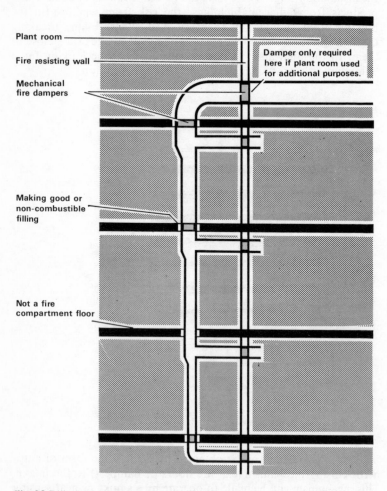

Fig. 20.7 Illustration of use of fire dampers (in unencased ductwork).

The mechanical damper in Fig. 20.8 consists of a hinged steel plate set in a steel frame. The metal used needs to be sufficiently heavy to prevent possible distortion due to heat. It should also be suitably treated to prevent corrosion in the environment in which it is to be used.

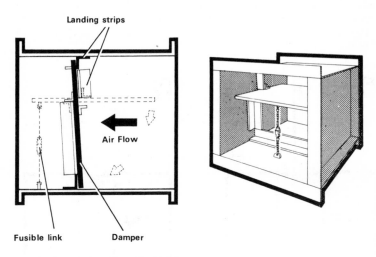

Fig. 20.8 Illustration of mechanical damper.

Mechanical dampers can be held in the open position by:

(i) A fusible link

   or

(ii) an electro-magnetic device (a solenoid).

The fusible link is usually set to operate at about 68°C. It is important that it is exposed to the air stream and is not shielded in any way by the damper blade.

The electro-magnetic device is normally operated by a smoke detector, which can be arranged to operate either all the dampers in a system or just a particular damper (or dampers). It is important where smoke detectors are used that they are installed in positions in which they are likely to give the quickest response. In many instances this may mean installing them in a room or other part of the building rather than in the ducting itself.

On operation of the detector or fusible link the damper closes automatically. When closed it should fit closely against its landing strip or seating, allowing sufficient clearance for possible expansion.

Other types of mechanical damper which work on the basic principle described above are shown in Figs. 20.9(1) and (2) (the shutter type is also illustrated in Plates 42 and 43).

Mechanical dampers fitted in a vertical position are gravity closed; where they are fitted in a horizontal position they are closed by means of a spring fitting. An elaboration of the conventional damper using power operation, such as compressed air, has been adopted in some cases. By this means whenever the plant shuts down, all fire dampers close. The system can also be coupled to smoke detectors to cause the dampers to close when a certain amount of smoke is present.

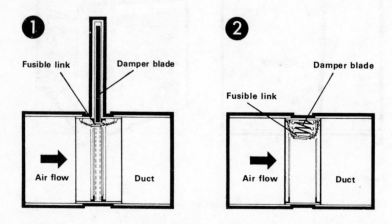

Fig. 20.9 (1) Sliding mechanical damper; (2) Shutter type mechanical damper.

Another development is the intumescent coated honeycomb damper. These honeycomb dampers are fixed into the ducting as shown in Fig. 20.10. When the system is in a healthy condition the damper allows free passage of air through the duct.

On heating, however, the intumescent paint will expand to approximately 100 times its original volume and form a solid mass thus preventing the passage of smoke through the duct (Plates 44, 45 and 46).

The intumescence of the paint is not affected by fluff or oil spray. It should however be kept free from greasy dirt and condensation or wetness which will interfere with its effectiveness.

Intumescent honeycomb dampers are more likely to be used in duct sections where the air velocity is low (e.g. at the outlet of ventilation ducts to rooms or compartments).

There are two reasons for this:

(i)   The lower the velocity of the air in the vicinity of the damper, the smaller the loss of head in the air flow. (It should be remembered that the intumescent damper is permanently in the air flow—in the normal state metal dampers are not).

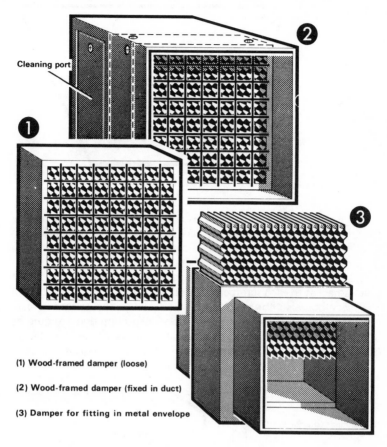

Cleaning port

(1) Wood-framed damper (loose)

(2) Wood-framed damper (fixed in duct)

(3) Damper for fitting in metal envelope

Fig. 20.10 Intumescent-coated honeycomb dampers. (1) Wood-framed damper (loose) (2) Wood-framed damper (fixed in duct) (3) Damper for fitting in a metal envelope.

(ii) If placed in the path of high velocity air the melting paint may be sucked towards the unexposed face of the damper due to the pressure difference on either side. This can obviously reduce its effectiveness.

Additional support for the honeycomb is needed if it is fixed in a horizontal position (Fig. 20.11). This is to prevent sagging when the paint begins to melt in a fire condition.

Intumescent dampers will provide 40 minutes to 1 hour fire resistance depending on their thickness. Single metal dampers will normally provide up to 2 hours fire resistance. For higher standards double dampers can be used if a single damper of the required standard is not available.

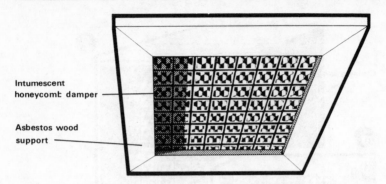

Fig. 20.11 Illustration of honeycomb damper fitted in horizontal position.

Regular inspection of dampers is necessary. This is particularly so with mechanical dampers. They may remain inactive for many years when the pivots, landing strips etc. can accumulate dust or dirt which would prevent, or delay, operation of the damper.

Inspection doors (Fig. 20.12) must therefore be provided in the duct adjacent to each damper. This allows not only for inspection of dampers but also for replacement of fusible links or intumescent dampers after they have operated. These inspection doors should be fitted with locks and have a fire resistance similar to the shaft enclosure. (If the standard of fire resistance of the shaft enclosure does not

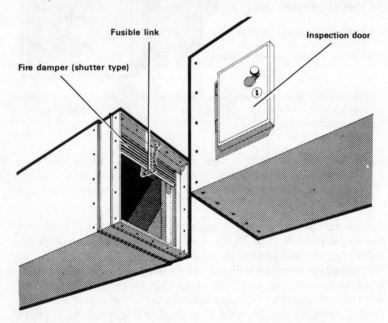

Fig. 20.12 Diagram of duct showing inspection door adjacent to fire damper.

need to exceed one hour, the fire resistance of access doors can be half that of the enclosure).

(3) Fire stopping of shafts (encased ducting)

Where ducts are encased in shafts the possibility exists of smoke, heat or flame spread through the shaft itself. To avoid this, non-combustible infilling should be inserted around the duct where it breaches each fire compartment floor, so that a permanent seal is provided. If the duct is enclosed in a shaft with fire-resisting walls, a solid non-combustible filling need only be provided, at most, every 10 metres (Fig 20.13(1)). As an alternative, a permanent vent can be created at the top of the shaft; the solid non-combustible filling is not then required (Fig. 20.13(2)).

(In *unencased* ducting, infilling AND the provision of dampers is necessary where the duct breaches each fire compartment floor, see Fig. 20.7.)

Non-combustible infilling is also needed where any pipe passes through a fire-resisting duct-shaft. Pipes with small internal diameters are also recommended for this situation; should they perish in a fire the minimum gap is thereby left for the passage of smoke, heat and flame.

4 Recirculation systems

In these systems a given supply of air (up to 75 per cent in some situations) is constantly recycled through the plant room. It can be appreciated therefore that smoke entering such a system can be quickly spread throughout a building, possibly jeopardising means of escape and hindering fire fighting operations.

Except in small plants or small buildings, therefore, a device, normally a smoke detector, should be installed in the extract ducting before the point where the air is separated. In the event of appreciable quantities of smoke being detected in the system, the detector will cause the re-circulation of air to cease and either discharge the return air outside the building or shut down the plant automatically. Some systems have the expensive alternative of smoke extract fans in addition to the normal fans.

In either case, a device, capable of being operated by firemen, should be installed in a position agreed by the fire authority to enable the plant to be stopped. Where practicable it may also be desirable to have a device which would enable the firemen to start the system again when it is considered necessary to clear the building of smoke. In large buildings with a number of plant rooms these facilities may be found in a central control room where firemen can possibly seek the assistance of engineers when dealing with a technically complex system.

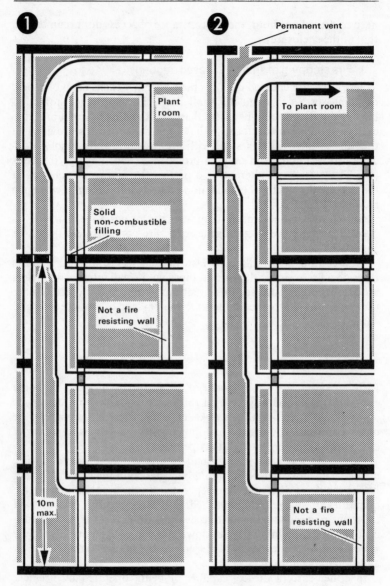

Fig. 20.13 (1) A duct shaft with non-combustible filling (2) a duct shaft with roof vent.

Summary

This summary is produced in the form of questions Fire Prevention Officers will want answered when considering the installation of air-conditioning or ventilation systems in buildings.

The questions are not intended to be fully comprehensive but to serve as a guide to the main areas which need consideration (in conjunction of course with other fire prevention aspects such as means of escape).

(i) Are ducts properly sited (e.g. are ducts for special risks separate from the main system)?

(ii) Is the material being used for the ducting and insulation acceptable in accordance with British Standard 476 etc?

(iii) Are flexible joints and connections necessary—if so are they being used in accordance with recommended practice?

(iv) Are air intakes safely sited?

(v) To what extent are fire dampers and infilling or venting of shafts required?

(vi) If automatic fire detection equipment is to be used in the ducting —is the type chosen suitable for the risk involved?

(vii) Where a recirculation system is to be installed, can the recirculation effect be halted in the event of a fire?

(viii) Is the system (irrespective of type) capable of being operated both automatically and manually? (This can help to ensure that movement of air is halted as quickly as possible after the outbreak of fire).

(ix) When shut down, can the system be readily restarted, wholly, or in part, to extract smoke etc.?

(x) What type of filter is being used?—(If dry, is it flammable; if viscous, has the oil a flash point NOT LESS than 177°C; if electrostatic, is there an isolation switch?)

Conclusion

It has been found by experience that the individual systems of ventilation and air conditioning require individual study and treatment to make them as safe as possible. The basic points described in this chapter will generally be applicable, however, when plans of new buildings to be installed with ventilation or air-conditioning systems are being inspected.

Chapter 21
Pressurisation of staircases

In multi-storey buildings, staircases and lobbies are a very important part of the means of escape. Smoke and hot gases in a fire situation, are the main dangers to escape routes and in order to clear any smoke that may penetrate the route some form of ventilation has always been insisted on. Two means of ventilation have traditionally been available:

(i) Permanent vents

(ii) Openable windows.

Experience has shown that these methods do have disadvantages. Permanent vents, for example, large enough to serve their function can also cause extremely unpleasant conditions at other times. If the alternative of openable windows is used smoke logging may occur before there is an opportunity to open them—due to the rapid build-up of smoke in the early stages of a fire. This problem can be overcome by causing the necessary windows for cross ventilation to open on operation of smoke detectors. Such a scheme has been installed and proved satisfactory in tests.

Nevertheless, any form of natural ventilation is dependent for its effectiveness on wind speed and direction. Research has shown that ideal wind conditions in any situation can only be expected for about 50 per cent of the time. A system of natural venting in multi-storey buildings may not therefore give 100 per cent performance when required. Localised wind conditions around tall buildings can also complicate the issue.

All these points bring the efficiency of natural ventilation into question. In addition, the desire of architects to install centre core staircases has meant that some alternative to natural ventilation has had to be found.

Mechanical extract systems fitted in staircases would rapidly clear any smoke or toxic gases penetrating that area. On the other hand, the fact that they would be extracting air along with the smoke could quickly give rise to a lower pressure existing in the staircase than in the fire area. This could lead to a more rapid build up of smoke, increasing the hazard rather than reducing it.

Pressurisation, however, has now been proved to be a practicable means of protecting stairs and lobbies from invasion by smoke.

1   What is pressurisation ?

Pressurisation is the name given to the technique of creating a higher pressure in an escape route by mechanical ventilation, thus preventing the ingress of smoke and toxic gases. The most common means of achieving pressurisation is by centrifugal or axial fans driven by an electric motor. The fans are connected to a duct system with output grilles. These grilles can be sited at each floor level, alternate floors or every five floors (say), depending on the requirements in the particular building. Fire dampers must not be fitted in pressurisation ducting—for obvious reasons—an uninterrupted flow of air is needed when the system is operative.

A pressurisation system can be used in one of three ways:

(i)   Only in the event of fire (provision for automatic AND manual starting is desirable).

(ii) On full duty when the building is occupied.

(iii) At reduced capacity when the building is occupied with automatic (and manual) boost to full duty in the event of fire.

Which method is chosen will depend on the nature of the building, its occupancy and of course the economics of the situation. Table 9, however, gives some guidance on suggested operating schedules.

Table 9

Suggested schedule of operation for pressurisation systems

Occupancy	Alarm system	Mode of operation
Typical office accommodation	Manual or automatic	Plant normally off. Operates on alarm being raised.
With sleeping accommodation	Automatic smoke detectors	Plant normally off. Operates on activation of alarm.
	Manual alarm	Plant at reduced capacity. Boost to full capacity on alarm being raised.

(Reprinted from Fire Research Note No. 958.)

2 Requirements of a pressurisation system

The two basic requirements or considerations when designing a pressurisation system are:

(a) the pressure required in the staircase and/or lobby

(b) the leakage paths.

a. The pressure required

If a pressurisation system is to be effective it must, by definition, achieve a higher pressure than that developed by the fire and weather conditions. The recommended level of pressurisation for this country is 5 mm water gauge. This represents ten times the pressure developed in a fire and is four times the maximum pressure likely to be caused by adverse weather conditions.

The air flow required to achieve this pressure is independent of the volume of the space to be pressurised. In deciding on the air flow required however it is necessary to take the leakage paths into account.

b. Leakage paths

Leakage paths, in the main, are those minor gaps around doors and windows which allow air to escape and they are a necessary part of any pressurisation system. Unless air is able to escape, the complete building becomes pressurised and the necessary pressure differential (i.e. between fire area and escape route) ceases to exist. Leakage paths can be discussed in two stages:

(1) the initial leakage path

(2) the final leakage path.

(1) The initial leakage path

In most instances this will be past the gaps around doors leading to individual rooms (Fig. 21.1). Badly fitting doors will create too large a leakage path and can unbalance the system. The maximum recommended gap is 3 mm.

Research has shown that a 50 per cent increase in leakage area approximately halves the pressurisation attained with a given supply rate. This helps to emphasise the importance of good fitting doors for effective pressurisation.

In a fire situation, of course, people will have to exit through such doors. This momentary opening of doors does not seriously affect the pressurisation system, and any pressure lost is quickly recovered when the door is closed again. Doors left permanently open will obviously weaken the system.

Incidentally, pressurisation of 5 mm w.g. will mean that extra pressure is required to open a door leading to the pressurised area. This pressure is sufficiently small to allow most people to open doors with only slightly increased effort.

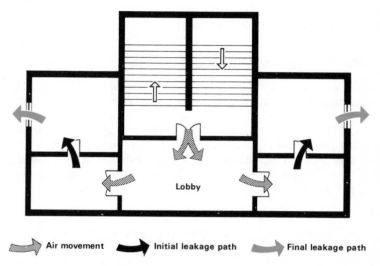

Air movement   Initial leakage path   Final leakage path

Fig. 21.1 Illustration of leakage paths.

(2) The final leakage path

As shown in Fig. 21.1 this is through the gaps in an openable window. In practice there will generally be sufficient leakage past such windows for pressurisation purposes. If the windows are weatherstripped a supplementary form of leakage or venting may be necessary.

Other forms that can be used are:

(i)   vents in external walls (normally kept closed and released only on operation of the pressurisation system. Useful in double-glazed or 'sealed' buildings),

(ii) mechanical extract systems (but can conflict with fire protection measures explained in the first part of this chapter),

(iii) natural ventilation (using a vertical shaft with openings at the top and on each floor. These are normally kept closed and released on operation of the pressurisation system).

3 Stack effect

This is the name given to the situation in which cold air outside a building and warm air inside a building can create a constant flow of air up a stairway. This can interfere with a pressurisation system. As there is not a wide temperature range in this country—stack effect is not troublesome.

Where it is troublesome it can be overcome by providing pressurising inlets at each floor level or by breaking the stairway into sections with doors at (say) every 5th floor.

4 What areas should be pressurised ?

Ideally the complete escape route from fire area to exit should be pressurised. In this country however, the choice has always been between the staircase or lobby. Generally it is the staircase that is chosen. If, however, the lobby is part of the leakage path it will also become pressurised to a certain extent. To pressurise both the staircase and lobby is practicable but would obviously require higher pressures. The final decision on the extent of pressurisation to be used will normally be based on:

(i)   the nature of the building itself and

(ii) the economics of the situation (i.e. cost related to possible benefits).

Conclusion

The objective of a pressurisation system is to achieve an excess pressure in the escape route in order to prevent the entry of smoke and toxic gases in a fire situation. The recommended pressure is 5 mm w.g. The air input required to achieve this pressure is calculated on the area of the leakage paths (which are necessary for the effectiveness of the system)—it is not affected by the volume of the space to be pressurised.

Although no Code of Practice on pressurisation exists, in general terms the reliability of mechanical ventilation in comparison to natural ventilation is one of the main points in favour of the system. The development of higher buildings, both for office and living accommodation, presents problems in the protection of escape routes which in many cases can best be met by pressurisation.

From a practical fire-fighting viewpoint a pressurised staircase or lobby can be advantageous to firemen establishing a bridgehead for fire fighting.

Glossary and terminology

Brief definitions are given below of some of the terms used in connection with automatic fire detection and alarm systems with which you may be unfamiliar.

'Closed' circuit system
An electrical circuit in which the contacts of detectors and call points are normally 'closed'. When a detector or call point is actuated current flow is interrupted to sound the alarm.

'Fixed temperature' detector
A heat detector that responds only when a predetermined temperature is reached.

Integrated circuit
A miniature electronic circuit designed to perform a specific function.

Integrator
A component designed to respond only when the average of the individual signals it receives over a period reaches a predetermined level.

Line fire detector
(Line detector)
A form of fire detector which responds to the phenomenon detected anywhere along its length.

'Open' circuit system
An electrical circuit in which the contacts of detectors and call points are normally 'open'. When a detector or call point is activated the circuit is completed to sound the alarm.

Point fire detector
(Point/spot detector)
A form of fire detector which responds to the phenomenon detected at a fixed point.

'Rate-of-rise' detector
A heat detector that responds when the temperature rise is abnormally rapid.

Relay
A form of automatic switch which is actuated by passing an electric current through the coil of an electro-magnet.

Terminology—New terms which you will find in 'Fire extinguishing systems'.

Foam Concentrate
The foam liquid as supplied by the manufacturer. Previously known as as foam compound.

Foam Solution
A solution of foam concentrate in water at the appropriate concentration.

Further reading

In order that students may further improve their knowledge the following associated material is listed and grouped under the Part headings of this volume.

Fire extinguishing systems

Fire Research Note—No. 1003
'Experimental appraisal of an American sprinkler system for the protection of goods in high racked storages'.

Fire Research Note—No. 1016
'The effect of a sprinkler on the stability of a smoke layer beneath a ceiling'.

Building Research Establishment Current Papers:

CP 68/74—'The rapid extinction of fires in high rack storages'.

CP 25/75—'Problems with the use of fire-fighting foams'.

CP 29/75—'The performance of the sprinkler in detecting fire'.

CP 42/75—'Fire protection of flammable liquid storage by water'.

CP 67/75—'The performance of the sprinkler in the extinction of fire'.

CP 79/75—'The essentials of sprinkler and other water spray fire protection systems'.

CP 98/75—'The performance of a foam-sprinkler installation on simulated oil rig fires'.

CP 50/76—'The use of automatic sprinklers as fire sensors in a chemical plant'.

CP 52/76—'Sprinkler systems for special risks'.

British Standard 5041: Fire hydrant systems equipment.

Fire alarm systems

Building Research Establishment Current Papers:

CP 32/75—'The behaviour of automatic fire detection systems'.

CP 38/75—'Current research of fire detection at the Fire Research Station'.

British Standard—5839 Pt. 1—'The installation and servicing of electrical fire alarm systems'.

Rules of the Fire Offices' Committee for 'Automatic Fire Alarm Installations'.

British Standard 3116:

Part 1   Heat sensitive (point) detectors

Part 2   Heat sensitive (line) detectors

Part 3   Smoke sensitive detectors

Part 4   Control and indicating equipment.

(Parts 2 and 3 are still in the course of preparation.)

Joint Fire Research Organisation:

Symposium No. 6	Automatic fire detection.
Fire Research Note No. 770	Experiments on smoke detection, Part 1—'Flammable liquid fires'.
Fire Research Note No. 780	Experiments on smoke detection, Part 2—'Fires in wood cribs, rubber cribs, polyvinyl chloride powder and petrol'.
Fire Research Note No. 793	The detection of fires by smoke, Part 2—'Slowly developing wood crib fires'.
Fire Research Note No. 810	'The behaviour of automatic fire detection systems'.

Fire venting systems

British Standard Code of Practice:

CP 352—'Mechanical ventilation and air conditioning in buildings'.

CP 413—'Ducts for building services' (particularly Appendix A).

CP 3   — Chapter IV (Parts 1, 2 and 3—'Precautions against fire'.

Building Standards Regulations 1972—relevant sections only.

Fire Research Note No. 5 (J.F.R.O.)—'Fire venting in single-storey buildings'.

Fire Research Technical Paper—No. 10—'Design of roof venting systems for single-storey buildings'.

Fire Prevention Guide No. 1 'Fire precautions in town centre developments'. HMSO.

Fire Research Memoranda:

Memorandum No. 84
Memorandum No. 90   Tests of ventilation duct fire dampers constructed from intumescent-coated honeycombs—Parts I, II and III.
Memorandum No. 99

Fire Research Notes:

Note 850—'Smoke tests in pressurised stairs and lobbies in a 26-storey building'.

Note 859—'Intumescent matrices as fire resistant partitions'.

Note 958—'Pressurisation of escape routes in buildings'. (This is a useful survey of the principal research that has taken place.)

A structured text on automatic fire detection and alarm systems is available which has been prepared by and is available from the Home Office Unit for Educational Methods, Moreton-in-Marsh, Gloucestershire.

Manual of Firemanship
Revised Structure

Book 1 Elements of combustion and extinction

Part	Part	Chapter	First published
1 Physics of combustion	1	1	1943
2 Chemistry of combustion	1	1	1943
3 Methods of extinguishing fire	1	2 and	1945
	6A	32(III)	1945

Book 2 Fire brigade equipment

Part	Part	Chapter	First published
1 Hose	1	4	1943
2 Hose fittings	1	5	1943
3 Ropes and lines, knots, slings ,etc	1	7 and	1943
	6A	39	1945
4 Small gear	1	13	1943

Book 3 Fire extinguishing equipment

Part	Part	Chapter	First published
1 Hand and stirrup pumps	1	8	1943
2 Portable chemical extinguishers	1	9	1943
3 Foam and foam-making equipment	1	10	1943

Book 4 Pumps and special applicances

Part	Part	Chapter	First published
1 Pumping appliances	2	1	1944
2 Practical pump operation	2	2	1944
3 Special appliances	2	6	1944

Book 5 Fire brigade ladders

Part	Part	Chapter	First published
1 Extension ladders	1	6	1943
2 Escapes and escape mountings	2	3	1944
3 Turntable ladders	2	4	1944
4 Hydraulic platforms	2	5	1944

Book 6 Breathing apparatus and resuscitation

Part	Part	Chapter	First published
1 Breathing apparatus	1	11	1943
2 Operational procedure	6A	32(V)	1945
3 Resuscitation	1	12	1943

Book 14 Special Fires I

Part		Part	Section	First published
1	Fires in animal and vegetable oils	6C	8	1962
2	Fires in fats and waxes	6C	3	1962
3	Fires in resins and gums	6C	13	1962
4	Fires in grain, hops, etc	6C	6	1962
5	Fires in fibrous materials	6C	4	1962
6	Fires in sugar	6C	15	1962
7	Fires in paints and varnishes	6C	9	1962

Book 15 Special Fires II

Part		Part	Section	First published
1	Fires in dusts	6C	1	1962
2	Fires in explosives	6C	2	1962
3	Fires in metals	6C	7	1962
4	Fires in plastics	6C	10	1962
5	Fires involving radioactive materials	6C	11 and	1962
		6A	Chap 33 (6)	1945
6	Fires in refrigeration plant	6C	12	1962
7	Fires in rubber	6C	14	1962

Book 16 Special Fires III

Part		Part	Chapter	First published
1	Fires in rural areas	6B	1	1946
2	Fires in electricity undertakings	6B	3	1946
3	Fires in aircraft	6B	4	1946

Book 17 Special Fires IV

Part		Part	Section	First published
1	Fires in fuels	6C	5	1962
2	Fires in oil refineries	6B	Chap 5	1946
3	Fires in gasworks	6B	Chap 2	1946

Book 18 Dangerous substances

	Part	Section	First published
Alphabetical list of dangerous substances	6C	16	1962

Printed in the UK for HMSO
Dd737175 C50 2/84 (1)

NOTES

NOTES

NOTES

NOTES